What the readers say about *Every S*

'A fascinating read' Billy Hopkins, best se[...]
Hopes, *Kate's* Story, *Going Places* and *Any[...]*

'A tragicomic masterpiece' Fr Brian Seale, Salford Diocese, author of
The Moston Story

'Every sentence a tonic – bringing back many memories from my
childhood . . . I savour every page. I'm reading it slowly because I don't
want it to end' Martin McCawley, Bolton, Greater Manchester

'It really puts me back there in my Manchester days. I can't wait to get
back to it. It's like a trip home' Barbara Cunningham (*née* Doubleday),
Atlanta, Georgia, USA

'I can recommend this book for its wit, humour, and down to earth
honesty . . . It made me laugh, it made me cry, but most of all it made me
happy' Mary Luke (*née* Sidlow), Blackley, Manchester

'I had a really good laugh' George Krystek, Cheadle

'Entertaining from the first page to the last' Janet Driver, Santa Monica,
California, USA

'Liked the local history bits' Tony Coogan, Middleton

'Thanks for the book, reading it in bed at 5 am this morning . . . makes
me laugh out loud . . . love it' Lynda Goodfellow (*née* Estall), Unsworth,
Greater Manchester

'Just wanted to let you know that . . . what you wrote . . . is perfect' Kim
Caffrey, Shelby Township, Michigan, USA

'Your book will have an honoured place in my bookcase . . . with Billy
Hopkins' books' Edna Wright, Middleton, Greater Manchester

The Avenue Cinema, 1958

MANCHESTER KISS

Shops, junction of Rochdale Road//Middleton Old Road, 1958

BILL KEETH

Limited Edition Press

First Published in 2006
by
Limited Edition Press
No.10@59, M16 7RQ

by the same author:
Every Street in Manchester

DISCOGRAPHY

'Elizabethan Serenade' (Ronald Binge) by Ron Goodwin &
His Concert Orchestra is on Parlophone 45-R 4272

'The Hungry Years' (Sedaka/Greenfield) by Neil Sedaka is on
Polydor 2059 113, 1975

All other titles are amply documented in
the *Record Collector Rare Record Guide,*
the *Guinness Book of British Hit Singles,* and
British Record Charts, 1955-1979 (pub. Macdonald/Futura)

Cover photograph: pavement, north Manchester

To anyone who ever bought a ha'penny chew
at Mr Mac's shop on James Street -
especially those brave souls who went over
the school wall in order to do so.

The Red Lion, Rochdale Road, 1972

We for a certainty are not the first
Have sat in taverns while the tempest hurled
Their hopeful plans to emptiness, and cursed
Whatever brute and blackguard made the world.

A.E. Housman: *Last Poems*

Confectioner's, junction Charlestown Road/
Rochdale Road, 1968

Author's Note

The photographic images accompanying the text of *Manchester Kiss* are readily available to visitors to the Archives and Local Studies Department at Manchester Central Library*. They are representative of the work of Lawrie Kaye, Thomas Brooks and L. H. Price, three members of Manchester Amateur Photographic Society (MAPS), which - when widespread housing clearances were in the offing in Manchester from the 1950s onwards - arranged for its members to preserve a photographic record of the city as it then was.

In the present instance the shots are intended to illustrate *Manchester Kiss*, though they might with equal justification be said to illustrate *Every Street in Manchester*, the novel that precedes it. Roughly half their number illustrate a bus journey along Rochdale Road, the A664, towards Manchester city centre that occurs in Chapter 2 of *Manchester Kiss*, whilst the second half of the collection records Shirlee Jameson's homeward journey via that same bus route in Chapter 8 of *Every Street in Manchester*.

* See www.images.manchester.gov.uk or pay a personal visit to the Archives and Local Studies Department at Manchester Central Library.

Tel: 0161 234 1979 Local Studies; 0161 234 1980 Archives

E-mail: archiveslocalstudies@manchester.gov.uk

Opening hours Monday to Thursday 9 am to 8 pm; Friday and Saturday 9 am to 5 pm. Hours for booking and viewing material in the Archives section are Monday to Thursday 9 am to 4 pm only.

Sincere thanks to Manchester Archives and Local Studies Department for permission to reproduce these photographic images of the postal district of Manchester 9 (Blackley, Harpurhey and Collyhurst) and for invaluable assistance in preparing them for publication.

1

Bookless in Benidorm

Sitting down at my PC, which as late in the day as yesterday afternoon would see me pre-occupied with the completion of a first novel (keep the champagne on ice awhile: the life-work of my favourite writer can be measured by the linear foot, four of them), I feel at a bit of a loss – almost as if there had been a death in the family (which, as a matter of fact, there has been). All I really want to do is to sit in the shade in the sun for seven days somewhere in the Canary Islands with George V. Higgins of Boston, Massachusetts.

Not that Mr Higgins knows me, or will ever do, for Mr Higgins died some time ago (another death in the family). No, George V. Higgins is known to me simply because he very obligingly left behind him a substantial body of work (two and a half linear footsworth), much of which I have read over the years, plus a further eight titles I managed to access before Christmas via www.abebooks.com (Advanced Book Exchange of Victoria Island, British Columbia) with a view to taking them to the Canaries with me.

The bookshop I normally use in Manchester city centre had shown itself capable of assisting me with just 12½ per cent of my George V. Higgins order. And interestingly enough (well, I think it is), amongst the full 100 per cent quota (i.e. the eight books) I received via www.abebooks.com came a brand new copy of one Higgins title that was billed to me (ex-New York, New York, inclusive of post and packing) for £3 less (yes, I've done the currency conversion) than that same bookshop in Manchester city centre could have supplied it for had I presented myself to pay/ collect at its fiction desk five weeks down the line – this representing its 12½ per cent capability in the matter.

I have probably overdone it with eight books by George V. Higgins for holiday reading. But better too many books than too few, I always say – that is, if you can get me to say anything other than: 'Shhhh!' while I'm about it. Oh, I can read a book a day on holiday easily enough (seven Rumpoles, seven by Dick Francis maybe), but George V. Higgins' books are literature of a different order; and when I say this I am not referring to the fact that George V. Higgins' books are consistently misfiled under 'Crime' at every bookshop on the planet. No, what I really mean to say is that George V. Higgins' books are literature *per se*, irrespective of genre. So Mr Higgins' books take – heck, Mr Higgins' books deserve – a modicum of mastication prior to digestion, which is not to say they are unreadable; they are the exact opposite of that.

Of course, there are certain types of holiday that do not lend themselves to the book-a-day syndrome with which I am afflicted – for example, any holiday that involves sightseeing on a grand or epic scale: London, Paris, Venice, the American West, the Australian Outback, McMurdo Sound. (By the way, I've not yet seen these last three, I hasten impecuniously to add.) But at times like these I will opt instead for a solitary volume that is in some way connected with my projected destination. Thus, Miles na Gopaleen, aka Flann O'Brien (aka Brian O'Nolan too), shipped out to Dublin's fair city with me, whilst W. (William) Stanley Moss and Paddy Leigh Fermor awaited my arrival in Heraklion with *Ill Met By Moonlight* and patience incomparable. (General Kreipe, it seemed, was still in residence at the Villa Ariadne, albeit only temporarily once my Air 2000 flight touched down.) But the best I could come up with for Lido de Jesolo, my base for a visit to Venice last June, was a re-reading of *Dubliners* – Trieste, where James Joyce lived for many years, being just a ferry boat ride away across the Adriatic. This last choice of reading matter was to pay an unexpected dividend.

I came back from Lido determined to finish a novel I'd been messing about with for far too long, set myself a regimen and a target date for completion, then overran the completion date by three months. Nevertheless, eight months on (yesterday afternoon to be precise) – hey presto! – finished! And now an eternity before I find a publisher. And so to work.

I do occasionally come unstuck with holiday reading matter.

A few years ago I found myself bookless in Benidorm, and it seemed to me that perhaps the weekly street market at Finestrat at the far end of town might alleviate my distress. There were books galore at the street market at Finestrat, plus a 'Bring 'Em Back A-read And PX 'Em' bonus. No questions asked. Hey, and no questions asked by yours truly on my arrival on site, because the paperbacks on offer at this Catalan *ultima thule* were the self same horrorshow boom-bang-a-bang breast sellers that infest every street market on earth. There was just one glimmer of light in that sea of pesetas-purchasable pulp – a slimmish volume, it's true, but it looked very promising indeed. For one thing, it was marked up (or, rather, down) at the bargain-basement price of 100 pesetas; and, secondly, it carried a financial health warning, courtesy of the proprietor. To wit, *amigo*, should you be rash enough to blow your stash on this book, you were not going to be allowed to PX it. No way, *José*. Should you be daft enough to take this book on, you were going be stuck with it, which – I must say – I was delighted to be. Moreover, I shall never cease to wonder at my good fortune that day. Because the book *Diego* did not want and I most certainly did was *All Points North* by Simon Armitage. An absolute blooming bargain! (Oh, all right, I read it in a day or two, then fretted. But PX it? Hey – *¡Cuidado, Rodrigo!* Only if you throw in a gold doubloon as a make-weight!)

Nothing in this world affords me such a frisson of tight-wad smugness as donning Foster Grants to sit in the shade on some longed-for littoral, having stumped up £1000 for the holiday and a mere pittance for quality reading matter sufficient to keep me out of the mid-day sun yet content, Englishman though I be.

And interestingly enough (well, I think it is) Simon Armitage may be in very good company indeed – and I don't mean my own (though, naturally, I do). No, I refer to his secludedness, J. D. Salinger, or rather to the method by which Salinger is said to have selected his reading matter whilst serving with the American forces in Europe during World War II. For I am sure I remember reading somewhere in the sparse yet abundant cornucopia which is Salinger's entire opus that whenever the Folks Back Home sent a shipment of books to Our Boys Over There, he'd simply stand back whilst the regiment breezed through, snatching several thousand titles of choice, since the detritus, according to Salinger, would consist of the books he really wanted. And, judging by pricing policy at Finestrat, I reckon Simon Armitage (to locate him anachronistically for the sake of my argument) would have been a dead cert to grace Salinger's bookcase back at base.

Incidentally, I should perhaps point out that Lido de Jesolo is in an entirely different category as towns go, holiday or otherwise. Whenever I'd put my copy of *Dubliners* aside to order a cafe Americano in Lido, bar staff would fall over themselves to volunteer gratuitous comments about Joyce; whereas, on the last occasion I read Anthony Burgess in a cafe off Parsonage Gardens in his native Manchester and stopped to get an ice cream, people wanted to talk about espionage.

What miraculous covenant is it, I wonder, that has for so long protected Parsonage Gardens from the high-rise despoliation endemic elsewhere. I well remember finding them pleasant in the 1960s, walking through them five days a week on my way to work at the County Court on Quay Street; and I find them pleasant still, walking through them today to access a certain bookshop in Manchester city centre, though sadly, not George V. Higgins of Boston, Massachusetts.

And so to work.

Ah, but I am already at work: I have been at work for 1600 words and counting. I have simply called this piece 'Bookless in Benidorm', not 'Foreword', since it occurs to me that with a foreword I might lack not just Mr Higgins' company, but also your own.

So here we are, and, again, so to work – wishing you nevermore bookless in Benidorm, or anywhere else you care to holiday, with five good writers for company: Armitage, Joyce (with *Dubliners*, at any rate), Moss, O'Brien, and Higgins. Well, okay, seven: Dick Francis and John Mortimer are still under the beach towel, I see. But, 'Crime', remember: it would be a crime to miss out on George V. Higgins. Kick off with *Trust* and *Victories* (they go together), or any of the Jerry Kennedy books – or *The Friends of Eddie Coyle*. Leave the rest until you are used to the vintage.

¡Hasta la vista, amigo! ¡Una cerveza grande, por favor!

Why? What more do you want? Oh, all right, have a *coñac a limon*, if you must. But you're buying your own, I tell you. You can well afford to, the money I've saved you on a linear metre of good holiday reading matter with no *mierda* amongst it.

Bill Keeth

Middleton
Manchester

Gates of Boggart Hole Clough, foot of Valentine Brow, 1968

2

The Laughter That Never Came

The limited stop flashed by, leaving behind it an impression of well-scrubbed faces and a wake of rushing September air. Then the 72X came into sight on the brow of the hill, and for one moment it seemed as if it would hover there indefinitely. But, amidst a crashing of gears and a cloud of diesel fumes, the aged Crossley engine reasserted itself and the boy found himself having to run to catch it as it shuddered to a halt at Blackley Library bus stop located halfway along the convent wall.

He stepped aboard the inclined platform at the back of the bus and clung to the rail at the foot of the stairs, a school satchel across his shoulders, a cap set squarely upon his head, the angle of his body indicating his intention of ascending to the upper deck.

'Free pass is it, Einstein?' asked the bus guard good-humouredly, winking pointedly at a prissy-faced elderly woman with a blue rinse, perched a little uncomfortably, or so it seemed, on the rear seat nearest the bell, with a brace of shopping bags taking up the seat to the side of her. He scrutinised the plastic wallet the boy held ready in his hand and, reaching behind him without so much as a glance, located the bell, pressing it twice for the driver to proceed. 'Right you are, then,' he said as the bus got under way again, adding just loud enough for the passengers on the lower deck to share his good humour: 'But think on: no smokin' that dark shag o' yours up there. I've got a terrible chest this mornin'.'

Someone towards the front of the lower deck laughed aloud and one or two adult faces inclined themselves towards him and smiled. He was always good for a laugh George Ponden. (None of the passengers knew the guard's name, of course, but they knew the face all right.) George was the one who'd sing a selection of Josef Locke songs when the fancy took him and who'd been known to do 'Rudolf the Red-Nosed Reindeer' on the school bus in season.

But the boy felt his cheeks flush with embarrassment and,

with the bus lurching into motion, he clattered up the stairs as fast as he could, tumbling into the unoccupied back seat for fear that, had the interchange on the lower deck been funnelled, like himself, up the stairwell and past the reflection-distorting mirror at the head of it, the passengers on the upper deck might burst into ribald laughter upon his appearance amongst them.

Once he was in his place on the upper deck, puzzlement superseded his embarrassment. What was "shag", he wondered, and not for the first time. Because certainly from the way in which the word was muttered furtively in the playground at his new school and bandied about by older lads together with a slingshot of other four letter words – certainly, it was a rude word, though the boy had never imagined it to be connected with smoking. He had never, for that matter, succeeded in connecting the word with any other form of human activity – other than the cast-iron certainty, instinctively understood, that had he ever been foolhardy enough to utter the word at home (for purposes unimaginable) he would have received a swift clip round the ear-hole for his trouble and, beleaguered by the indignant query: 'Who've you been with?' would have been sent straight upstairs to bed.

What was "shag", he wondered – and more to the point, what was "dark shag"? For if "shag" were a rude word, "dark shag" must be so wicked as to be totally un-Christian. Perhaps it was one of the four sins which, according to the *Catechism of Christian Doctrine*, were said to be "crying to heaven for vengeance"? He began to list them in his head, getting no further than "defrauding labourers of their hire", a matter of some concern to him at the time because Stan the newsagent had shortchanged him by half-a-crown on the money due to him from his paper round. Okay, so it wasn't *his* paper round. (You had to be thirteen before you could have a paper round of your own, so he'd eighteen months to go yet.) It was Eddie's paper round. He'd been helping Eddie Bliss out with his paper round at the weekend, as he sometimes did when Eddie was going to Old Trafford on the Saturday afternoon and playing football himself on North End, off Dalbeattie Street, on the Sunday. But it was his *half-crown*, or rather it would be when Stan the newsagent got around to tipping up.

The boy stared sullenly at the shaved neck of the man in the seat in front of him, hating him, hating Stan the newsagent, hating the bus guard – hating all grown-ups, because they were so unreasonable and had secrets and kept them from you and knew so much more than you did and refused to explain things and, even when they made a pretence of explaining, gave you silly reasons that wouldn't have satisfied a child, a baby, that is. No he didn't, he decided: he didn't hate *all* grown-ups. He didn't hate his Uncle Ernie, did he? Uncle Ernie was funny. Uncle Ernie made him laugh with the silly things he said, silly things that were never meant to be taken seriously in the first place.

'What would you rather be or a wasp?' Uncle Ernie might say.

He had had to think long and hard about that one the first time Uncle Ernie had put it to him. To be fair though, he was only six years of age at the time.

Or Uncle Ernie would draw a rectangle in an upright position with a ten gallon hat on top of it, give it a downturned lip, no face, a neckerchief. 'Who's that?' Uncle Ernie would ask him then. But he knew the answer to that question too, because Uncle Ernie had done it so often. It was Oblong Cassidy, of course.

Sometimes Uncle Ernie would say something that made no sense at all, just because the words themselves sounded funny. 'Rob the rebel Ribble rubble rabble,' Uncle Ernie had muttered in his ear when their coach, one of Makinson's charas, had been held up by roadworks on the A59 outside Preston when they were on their way to Blackpool Illuminations last November.

But he hated all other grown-ups, he decided, his eyes becoming twin ray guns that bored remorselessly into the skull of the man with the shaved neck sitting in the seat in front of him. Oblivious to his fate, the man with the shaved neck turned to the back page of the *Daily Mess* to see what Whipcord had tipped for the 3.30 at Ayr. The boy intensified the death rays. Grown-ups! he thought in disgust. If it hadn't been for the bus guard making fun of him he'd have been able to march right down to the front of the bus and sit in the front seat; if it hadn't been for his mother going on at him at home he'd have been able to catch the limited stop at

Charlestown Road with Bazzo and Al Martino and Gibbo and Quelch.

'Mind you get the 72 like your dad says,' his mother had reminded him for the twentieth time that morning as they stood in the lobby at home. She took hold of his school tie and, as if her fingers knew some special magic, manipulated the knot he had made a pig's-ear of to a more appropriate size and resting-place. Then, as Ron Goodwin and his Concert Orchestra played 'Elizabethan Serenade' on the Light Programme on the wireless in the living room (a melody that would ever afterwards remind him of her) – *di-di-di-dih-di-di-di-dih* – she looked him up and down – *la-la-lah-la-lah-lah-lah-h-h* – removed a stray thread of cotton from his lapel – *la-la-la-la-la-lah-lah-lah-h* – and turned him round so she could inspect his back. He could see her face in the hall mirror. Her lips were set, unsmiling. She caught his eyes as she reached for the clothes brush that hung from the side of the mirror below the crossed palm fronds. 'Think on,' she said. 'You get the 72.'

'Aw, ma-a-m!'

He had been attending his new school, the grammar school in Rusholme, for a fortnight now, and this was to be the first time he was to be permitted to travel into town alone. Previously, to the boy's shame amongst his peers, his father had insisted on travelling into town with him on his way to the office. But today his father was off work with a temperature and the boy had set his heart on catching the limited stop with his friends.

'Aw, mam, everyone else goes down to Charlestown Road for the limited stop.'

'And one of these days,' said his mother, brushing his shoulders with vigorous downward sweeps as if to drive the meaning of her words deep within the marrow of his bones. 'And one of these days everyone else will get run over at Charlestown Road. You don't want to get run over, do you?'

True, this the boy did not want. But on this particular Monday morning in September, travelling into town on the 72 came streets ahead of this dread prospective event on his mental list of a whole variety of things he did not want.

'And tie that shoelace before you go out. Anyone'd think you'd been dragged up.'

He had not argued further, fully realising the futility of argument in the face of such paralysing logic. Obediently, he bent to tie the shoelace his mother put on a par with the monumental human carnage destined for Charlestown Road, his mind drifting to the projected scene of events where . . .

The limited stop – headlights blazing, throttle jammed, driver-less, guard-less, and brake-less – careered downhill from Victoria Avenue lights through a November pea-souper, negotiated at speed the left-hand bend opposite the Red Lion, and ploughed into, over, and through a queue of some fifty unfortunates who would have been better served by the 72.

Bazzo, Al Martino, Gibbo and Quelch had, the boy realised, caught the initial force of the impact. They lay together, their young lives prematurely extinguished, their lifeblood ebbing in a copious tide across Rochdale Road to access Boggart Hole Brook issuing from the Clough at the foot of Valentine Brow *en route* for the River Irk.

'Fire, ambulance,' he snapped into the handset of the squad car radio, deterring morbid bystanders and directing rush hour traffic flow with his other hand. 'You're gonna need cuttin' gear too from the looks o' things.' Removing his peaked uniform cap, he mopped his forehead with the back of his hand. 'Holy Cow!' he said to nobody in particular. 'There's blood everywhere . . .'

Then, with the bus jerking to a halt at Brewster Street opposite the Cintra Cinema the ray guns were re-directed temporarily at a man in a trilby hat who ascended the stairwell and seemed for a moment as if he might be about to sit on the back seat with him. This had the desired effect, causing the man in the trilby hat to wander further along the upper deck in search of a seat. And the bus was already trundling on its way again by the time the redundant death rays were re-directed at the temperance bar on the corner of Middlewood Street where . . .

In the chill darkness of a December night two pairs of powerful headlights arced across the neon-lighted entrance, illuminating briefly the Fedora-hatted, cigar-chomping, stripe-suited, ill-shaven, Peppermint Blitz-swilling clientele within. Two black sedans slewed violently on to the kerb and stopped. Somebody killed the lights. And for something less than sixty seconds Rochdale Road, Harpurhey, echoed with the shrill laughter of unsuspecting women. Then, as if on a given signal, the sedans disgorged their occupants – a dozen ill-assorted shadowy forms, hoods to a man, wiseguys: the Bazzomartino mob and that dirty stool pigeon, Quelch.

Spitting out the gum that had kept him company through the long hours of waiting, the boy turned up the collar of his off-white trench coat, slipped the safety-catch of his police issue Smith and Wesson (Here goes nuttin', he thought), and stepping soundlessly from the doorway of Timothy White's and Taylor's chemist's shop, he addressed himself to the glowing Havana on the opposite side of Rochdale Road.

'Okay, Big Baz, that's far enough. Hey, you too, Martino . . . Quelch. Ah'm takin' ya down da Twenny-Toid Precinct!'

By way of reply a solitary Thompson submachine-gun spat flame across the Queen's Highway and, somewhat regretfully, the boy discharged all six chambers of his police issue Smith and Wesson in rapid and lethal succession.

Patrolman Gibson was first on the scene in his black and white. 'Jeez, Chief,' he said, and kept on saying whilst the boy checked pulses and deflected grateful broads with his other hand. 'Jeez, Chief! Ya got all twelve of 'em. There's blood everywhere . . .'

And it was whilst the boy – borne aloft on the shoulders of an ecstatically-chanting, ticker-tape-festooned crowd – was being swept into the grounds of the White House to receive the Congressional Medal of Honor, this year's *Eagle* Annual, a dozen conkers, Typhoon Tyson's autograph, and a year's supply of Mars bars from President Eisenhower that a man bounded upstairs and sat in the seat beside him. This disturbed his reverie somewhat. And he found it even more disturbing in that, though the back seat might have accommodated three adults at a pinch, the newcomer had chosen to sit so close to him that he could scarcely move. He was aware too of an unusual smell about the man – a pungent

21

smell, something vaguely medicinal. What was it, he wondered, his mind flitting briefly between the Outpatients' Department at Booth Hall Children's Hospital, Balf's chemist's shop near Moston Lane corner and the changing rooms at his new school. And then he had it, he knew what it was: it was the smell of some kind of liniment.

The newcomer, the man who smelled of liniment, the man who now occupied the back seat on the upper deck with him, was sitting far too close to him for the ray guns to be profitably brought to bear on the problem, so he refocused them on the man in the trilby hat who – much to the boy's surprise – stood up immediately, walked the full length of the upper deck towards him, and descended the stairs. Then, via the man with the shaved neck sitting in the seat in front, the ray guns sought out those buildings on the block nearest to the Essoldo cinema where . . .

Within the dilapidated surgery with the dust-blown burgundy-painted front door that bore the polished brass shingle of an innocent Irish doctor, Baron Dr Fritz von Quelch, MD, Nuremburg (failed) was making his final preparations prior to commencing the first unanaesthetised human experiment of the day. The operating theatre had been rendered scrupulously clean by means of Dettol and a wire brush, and the Baron flicked an approving monocled glance at the instruments of medical research that glistened in sterile array in the dust-moted Collyhurst sunlight atop a workbench to which he himself had affixed the vice, the racking mechanism and the lathe. Monkey wrench, long-nose mole grips, Kango hammer, chainsaw, hayfork, and adze – yes, they were all ready to hand; these would take him through to his elevenses when he'd break for a cup of Hot Chocolate and a couple of Blue Riband biscuits. Baron Dr Fritz von Quelch, MD, Nuremburg (failed) adjusted his monocle, turned to his assistant and clapped his hands twice, his jack-booted heels clicking together involuntarily in the process.

At this signal a nurse (female apparently), her mouth set in a rictus like a crack in a Holland's pie crust, turned her attention from the mechanism of a mangle that had gone kaput and sped eagerly from the operating theatre to dragoon the first volunteer of the day.

It was not that the boy in the squalor of the rat-infested cell he shared with poor Louis was unaware of what was at stake. On the contrary, he had risen early in order to prepare himself. He had shaved at first light by means of a shard of glass, combed his hair with Axel grease (poor Axel, he and Bonhoeffer had defied the Reich once too often), and dressed in tropical whites. (He only wished his knees didn't look quite so knobbly in these kecks.) He had guessed she would come for poor Louis again.

'Madame,' poor Louis had croaked before he finally lost consciousness. 'Madame, you air so ug-lee zat eef effair you air kees-ed by ay 'an 'some preence, zee preence, 'e turn eento, ay, *grenouille* – 'ow you say eet, Ee-ngleesh? Ay frog!'

Fraulein Gudrun Gridironkampf would never forgive this insult.

'For mercy's sake, Fraulein,' snapped the boy as she barged into the cell and proceeded to kick the one-armed, one-legged Frenchman to his foot. 'For mercy's sake, Fraulein, take me in poor Louis' place. The Butcher operated on him only yesterday. There was blood everywhere. . .'

And it was at this precise moment that it happened.

Poor Louis was screaming at the full pitch of his lungs as the boy used every ounce of his St John's Ambulance Brigade know-how and a waterproof Elastoplast to staunch the flow of blood from the Frenchman's severed carotid artery when, inexplicably, Fraulein Gridironkampf turned her attention to the boy himself; seizing his right thigh so fiercely that it made him gasp – and had the effect of bringing him back to reality, where he realised with surprise amounting to horror that . . . there really *was* a hand on his leg. Not a daydream hand in a daydream world that could be zapped with Dan Dare's ray gun, run through with D'Artagnan's rapier, or biffed with a Freddie-Mills'-fisted right hook. No, the hand on his leg now was a real hand, a hand with substance – an adult's hand: the hand of the man sitting next to him. The man's hand was gripping his leg – agh! *stroking* his leg – in the smokey, swaying, creaking, crowded adult world of the upper deck of a number 72X bus on Rochdale Road, Collyhurst, at 8.32 am on a Monday morning in September in this Year of our Lord . . .

Ah, but no! For there can be *no* Year of our Lord for just as long as an adult will presume to do something of the sort to a little kid!

Quickly, the boy reviewed the information his senses were relaying to him. He could not feel the flesh of the palm of the hand: it was a hand within a pocket. He could feel the shape and strength and movement of the hand, but the texture of the hand was that of the interior lining of a trench coat pocket. Certainly, it was a powerful hand – it was a man's hand: it was *the* man's hand, the hand of the man sitting next to him – kneading and stroking and pinching the flesh of his right thigh immediately below the level of his short trouser leg. And with the smell of liniment seemingly stronger now than it had previously been, the boy imagined the hand to be a green hand, a green hand within a green pocket. He began to be very frightened indeed.

Then a succession of silly ideas ran through his head prior to his dismissing each in turn. It was Bazzo's dad playing a trick on him. But why on earth would Bazzo's dad want to do so? Mr Balanciaga had never so much as spoken two words to him in all the years he had known him. In any case, Mr Balanciaga worked in Oldham. So what would he be doing on a bus going into Manchester city centre at 8.32 am on a Monday morning in September?

Maybe it was Uncle Ernie, he thought. But, he knew instinctively in his heart of hearts that this wasn't the sort of trick his Uncle Ernie would play on him. Uncle Ernie would more likely say something like:

'Now, this is the upper deck, right? So, what do you call the downstairs on a bus?'

'What?'

'You heard us. What do you call the downstairs on a bus?'

'I dunno. The lower deck.'

'Yeah, you do. But I don't know either, because if this is the upper deck why don't they call the downstairs the downer deck? And if the downstairs on a bus is the lower deck why don't you call the upper deck the higher deck?'

He suddenly felt a great longing to see his Uncle Ernie, Mr E. E. Sidney as Uncle Ernie was known to the people who addressed the envelopes that dropped through his letterbox at the house on Borrowdale Road on Langley estate in Middleton where Uncle Ernie and Auntie Doreen had moved when their old house on Oakworth Street, near Tracy's tobacconist's shop in Blackley Village, was demolished.

Maybe it was a teacher from his new school, thought the boy. There *was* a teacher from his new school who used the number 72. The terminus of the number 72 was across the road from Grange Park Road where it met Charlestown Road immediately beyond the red brick wall of Booth Hall Children's Hospital – and the teacher, Mr Elmo Whitley, an old man who lived alone, lived in an end-terraced house on Charlestown Road, just past the hospital but before St John Bosco's church.

He steeled himself to take a sideways glance at the man sitting next to him, the man with the hand. This proved to be no easy task since the man with the hand was sitting so close to him and was so much taller than he was. Even so, gingerly – ever so gingerly – the boy turned his head to the right as far as he dared, inclining his eyeballs within their sockets so they squinted upwards at an angle of sixty-five degrees at the profile of . . . *a complete stranger.*

Instantly, the boy's mind regurgitated a terrible memory. Al Martino – Martin Casio, that is – Al Martino said there was this feller that strangled you and drank your blood and threw your body in a bath of acid, especially little kids.

Then his mind turned full circle. Could it really be happening? The man with the hand was staring directly ahead with pale, inexpressive eyes, and upwards of thirty grown-ups travelling into Manchester city centre on the upper deck of the number 72X bus had given no hint whatsoever that anything might be amiss. The man with the shaved neck had taken a propelling pencil from his inside breast pocket and was circling the name of the racehorse that Whipcord had napped. And – *yes!* – still the hand moved, the hand within the pocket, the green hand within the green pocket; still the hand within the pocket continued to fondle the boy's thigh.

His mouth had gone dry now; he swallowed with difficulty

and looked away, glancing out of the window and across to the railway goods yard at Thompson Street whence a little spur of track crossed Rochdale Road at its junction with Sudell Street *en route* for the Cooperative Wholesale Society's tobacco factory where, in happier times, the boy had waylaid Boer gold shipments – together with Mr Winston Spencer Churchill on one memorable occasion, an undertaking which had, in turn, led to another mutually satisfactory association in later years that had earned him the not-undeserved soubriquet, Junkers Jim of the Ardennes – or, more formally, Jimmy, Lord Harney of Blackley, VC, DSO, OBE, MC and bar.

He'd get off the bus immediately, he decided. No! – it was still a fair way into town, and the man with the hand might follow him. He was already pressed into the window, but he contrived to move even further. The hand stayed with him; and his heart sank.

There was nothing for it then. He would have to speak to this man; he would have to say something quiet and sensible, something that would clear up this misunderstanding at a stroke. He would have to say something that the thirty-odd adults on the upper deck of the 72X (including the man with the shaved neck who was shoving his newspaper, thrice-folded, into his jacket pocket now and seemed as if he might be preparing to get off) . . . he would have to say something that these adults on the upper deck with him would not feel inclined to laugh at. Yes, there was nothing for it other than that. He would have to say something that would have the effect of making the man with the hand remove it from his leg immediately.

He tried to think of sensible-sounding words, words that would have the desired effect. He willed his voice to assume a premature depth of expression, an enunciative maturity – Rock Hudson to speak; Ernest Borgnine to show. Words, their delivery, the most appropriate time to speak – these were the things that were uppermost in his mind as he neared the dread moment of necessary confrontation.

At New Cross, at the bottom end of Oldham Road, as the bus swung left on to Great Ancoats Street, across from the horse trough and opposite the Burton's branch at the top of Oldham

Street, George Ponden, intoning tunefully – *la-la-la-la-la-lah-lah-lah-la-lah-lah-la-lah-la-lah-lah-h-h* – began to mount the stairs for the last round-up – *di-di-di-dih-di-di-di-dih* . . . It would be best to speak, decided the boy, immediately the guard reached the head of the stairs. But when the guard reached the head of the stairs, everything happened at a speed that he could not have anticipated.

At the precise moment that George Ponden reached the head of the stairs and the boy was poised to speak the hand broke free of the pocket lining and touched the boy's thigh – flesh against flesh! And this, shocking him even more, had the effect of summoning his protest instinctively to his lips:

'Gerroff me *leg*, mister!'

He waited for the laughter that never came. Every adult head was turned towards him now, except for the man with the hand. The man with the hand was out in the gangway, trying to get to the stairs, where George Ponden – silent, stern-visaged too – steadfastly blocked his path. The man with the shaved neck was on his feet too. Barking savage words from deep within his throat, he hurled himself at the man with the hand and smashed his nose like an aubergine. There was blood everywhere and, suddenly, everyone was shouting at once. And as the bus swung into Newton Street past the Land o' Cakes, the boy found he had to take a dozen deep breaths to stop himself from being sick . . .

Heck! Three times as many deep breaths (or so it occurred to him five minutes later as he stood at the bus stop opposite Lewis's on Market Street, waiting for the No. 42 to take him to Rusholme), three times as many deep breaths as crack Royal Marine commandos (Bazzo, Al Martino, Gibbo and Quelch) with whom he had successfully sabotaged Bordeaux docks back in '42 thereby shortening the duration of the war by a full six months in the estimation of his old comrade in arms, who had been raised to the first office of state subsequent to the commencement of hostilities.

3

Summer in the Fifties

In them days of a summer Sunday . . .
motor cars,
green and black and heather blue,
clicked cool beneath the church wall
of early morning,
reflecting gargoyle children
from convex chrome
till our doctor, striding out of Mass,
boomed: 'Hello there, sunshine!'

In them days of a summer Sunday . . .
girls cried:
'Farmer, may we cross your golden river?'
whilst boys huddled at the kerb,
picking bubbled pitch between the setts,
moulding masks and men,
till this old woman screamed:
'Yous lot, get off the cart road!'

In them days of a summer Sunday . . .
Billy Cotton called
from open doors,
and through the gardens
wafted smells of cabbage and hot ovens
and New Zealand lamb,
arresting time,
till his band played:
'Somebody Stole My Gal.'

In them days of a summer Sunday . . .
old men
in belts and braces and voluminous pants
limped across cropped turf,
bent and bowled,
sweated and cursed
till they seen us and bellowed:
'Gerr-ar-to-vit!'

In them days of a summer Sunday . . .
golden girls,
long-legged, lissom, blinding in white,
leapt and ran
after a ball,
lobbing it over the net
and into it
till one of them, turning, asked:
'Well! D'yer wanna photer or summat?'

In them days of a summer Sunday . . .
rowdy lads
with Brylcreemed hair and vivid shirts
roped boats together
in convoy and sang
shanties on the lake,
mooring at the island,
laughing when this parkie moaned:
'Bleedin' young 'ooligans!'

In them days of a summer Sunday . . .
families
grouped at the bandstand by the brook
or climbed Angel Hill for free
and listened to the band and hecklers
in woodsmoke on the hill,
till this feller come up and grabbed one.
'Clever lad,' he said.
'Be a big help to your dad when you grow up.'

In them days of a summer Sunday . . .
an aeroplane,
single-engined like a fly,
droned above the wire works,
beating the bounds
of happiness
towards a westering sun
till me mam said:
'Your tea's on the table if you want it.'

4

To Carpetbagger, the *Fiducial Times*

Sir,

If my experience is anything to go by, your correspondent (*Portmanteau*, 5 April) would do well to temper his enthusiasm for his northern bank's move south with the thought that, whilst his northern bank is obviously intent on boxing the compass, there is evidence to suggest that it may be perfectly well prepared to let its customers' savings go west.

Ten years ago, in conjunction with a northern insurance company that is a household name, this same northern bank sold me an endowment policy with a projected maturity value of £6,900. That policy has recently matured, bringing me the grand total of just £4,556.29.

Now, I know interest rates are liable to fluctuation, and sometimes at an alarming rate; but what I simply cannot accept is that the Thatcher years have left this northern bank and its partner in grime with a cash shortfall in excess of 34%.

Consequently, I cannot help but wonder whether this northern bank has not been making a disproportionate portion of its own muckle with the mickles I was quite literally banking on to re-roof the house.

Yours etc.

Victor Jameson
Blackley, Manchester
26 April 1987

Carpetbagger says: *And all because you ignored my advice about life assurance – oft-repeated, I might add. So, I say again for the umpteenth time in as many years: Equitable Life, period.*

5

A Nameless Little Tune Without Words

'Tell us, Mr Harney,' said the parish priest softly, his voice a raft of sibilant understanding, 'what does your religion mean to you?'

At the opposite end of the refectory table, James T. Harney, B.Ed. (Hons; Class 2:1) shifted uncomfortably in his seat as the irritation welled within him like a wave. When he had submitted his application (prepared over the weekend of his birthday in November, neatly typed, duly signed) for the vacant headship of St Joseph of Cupertino's school, from which post Fred Swellands, his dad's partner at the nineteenth hole, was retiring at long last, the Governors of St Joseph's had failed to extend to him the simple professional courtesy of taking up his references from St Athelstan's where he had four years' experience as the deputy.

And, if truth be told, James Terence Harney had run St Athelstan's singlehandedly every summer term for the past three years when, on three consecutive annual occasions, Basil Hanlith, the head of St Athelstan's ('Skidpan Hanlith', as Harry Holwick, the school caretaker, had taken to calling him – a reference to the one and only Art and Craft class that Hanlith had taken during his ten years at the school) had contrived to crock himself, putting himself *hors de combat* until the September of the succeeding autumn term.

Back in July, 1972, Hanlith's Volswagen Beetle, pulling away from the kerb outside the North Parade on Victoria Avenue East, had collided with a Volvo saloon at 11.01 pm on the night of the dress rehearsal for the school show (*Hellzapoppin'*: Hanlith having assumed responsibility for the scenery for that production – scenery perpendicular, naturally, and, given his peculiar artistic flair, scenery horizontal too).

The following year had seen the accident at Bolton Abbey where Hanlith had fallen arse over tip and had to be hospitalized, the culprit in this instance being a tome of epic grandeur and quite spectacular format. For surely it must have seemed an impressive volume to the half dozen or so parents who were helping out on that day trip (one adult to six children), though Hanlith's staff were well-used (albeit not inured) to his self-preening. Said tome, hand-held by Hanlith for the duration of the trip, the more reverently to reveal its splendour to those around him, consisted of 962 pages, each of which held close to sixty lines of print except where the need for flow charts, pie charts and graphs set aside this arrangement. Furthermore – and this was truly the book's crowning glory – it was resplendent too with a title, vermilion-printed along its four-inch thick spine, vermilion-printed across the front of its Gollancz-yellow dust jacket, proclaiming the legend *Psychopaedagogy, Plowden and Beyond* to the world. Sadly, it did not take Hanlith beyond the stepping stones linking the left bank of the River Wharfe with the right. For midstream (from that point on the stepping stones, incidentally, where, a decade before that day, a nobbut-a-lad Richard Harris had courted a monochrome Rachel Roberts in the film version of David Storey's *This Sporting Life*) *Psychopaedagogy, Plowden and Beyond* toppled Hanlith into the River Wharfe where he drank his fill of the Dales prior to being hospitalized adjacent to the River Aire, emerging to pay a library fine of 32p on the 25 July, the feast day of St James the apostle.

The previous July Basil Hanlith, T.Cert. ('bleedin' R.D., you ask me' – this, again, from Harry Holwick of NUPE, who, had you happened to enquire what Harry meant by 'R.D.', would have replied 'bleedin' Readers' Digest, that's what!'), the previous July Hanlith had simply 'thrown a wobbler' (Harry) and had been ordered home by the inspectorate, 'foaming at the mouth' (Harry) . . .

. . . 'Basil Hanlith, temporarily; bloomin' inspectorate, permanently' – this last according to Fred Swellands, top-shelfing it one Sunday afternoon with Barry Harney in the clubhouse at Saddleworth Golf Club.

Fred Swellands also said he was 'glad to be getting out of it, Barry, but of course the lad's welcome to come and have a look round if he really must'. Fred Swellands had further – two stiff double Jameson's later – opined: ''T'were wise of the Authority not to term its inspectors "advisors" when the trendier authorities were doing that from the late-sixties on. More honest, if you like, Barry. Yeah, I'll give the buggers that. Because they don't blurry-well advise, do they, Barry? They inspect, pure and simple, and issue instructions. What was it Shaw said? "Those who can, do; those who can't, teach?" Bugger spoke too soon, you ask me, Barry. Because this lot we've got now take the bloomin' biscuit, they do. It's more like: "Those who don't teach and won't teach are forever telling those who do they're not doing it right and they're not doing enough . . ."'

'It's education, but not as we know it, Jim,' Fred Swellands had told him on his subsequent visit to St Joseph's as they completed a tour of inspection and returned to the office where they stood, talking, on the ground floor corridor next to a luxuriantly planted display of greenery below the trophy cabinet. 'You a fan of Star Trek, by any chance, Jim? . . . Well, not to worry . . . No, I don't mind it, as a matter of fact, Jim, but, heh, I'm more of a Virginian man, m'self . . . Set the colour up using Trampas' shirt: lovely shade of blue. Yes, I'm obligated to Doug McClure for that. The reds can be a bit iffy, you know . . . Oh, you will do, you swing this, Jim . . . Tell you when I fell. You remember that track event David Bedford won, led from the front all the way? You see that, Jim? . . . Ah! magic *is* the word, Jim; and even more magical in colour. I'd watched it in mono at home, and then I seen, saw it again in colour, that big Murphy Fr Elrick had in the presbytery before he, ah, went to his eternal reward. Heh, colour! Don't mind admitting it, Jim, I had to think for a moment. Is colour one of the dimensions? Heh. Because watching David Bedford cream it in colour, well, it was a completely different race, it seemed to me, and it had already been a completely different race in black and white. Tell you, I picked up a colour TV from Rumbelows the very next day: that shop across from Christ Church. Rented, you know. You know that white Murphy, they have – bit like the one they had in the presbytery before Fr Pavor was PP, only not as big. Tell you, I've never looked back, Jim; and with retirement coming up, you know . . . Recommend it for youngsters like you and Stella too. You're gonna be busy if you swing this headship, Jim. Get the girl a colour TV, stuck in with the kids of a night while you're out there empire building . . .'

. . . 'Chopping and changing the whole blurry time, this lot, Barry: the inspectorate. Got you pillar to post, they have. You can't do this, you can't do that; you must do it this way, you mustn't do it that; teachers always wrong, inspectors always right. Well, they would be, wouldn't they, Barry? Seeing how they never do nowt but moan. You never *do* nowt, you can't never get it wrong, can you, Barry? An' sod the double nuga . . . negatives. Nearly said "nugatory", Barry, burrit's not, is it Barry? Twice-bleedin'-over, it's blurry-well not nugatory. Same agair, B'rry. Mek man a double . . .'

. . . 'By the same token, Jim, as Charlie Wessenden used to say, man who never made a mistake, never made anything. Oh, it was tons different when I started at the chalk face, Jim. Emergency trained, just back from the War and raring to go. I remember old Charlie Wessenden, long gone now, God rest his soul, gassed in the first one, poor sod, I remember old Charlie Wessenden taking us to one side on my first day at All Vandals and Wreckers, heh: and he says, Charlie Wessenden says to us . . . heh, he was a star, was Charlie, Jim: "I want you to get in that classroom and teach, Swellands, me boy. Do whatever the hell you want to do in there, and, believe me, at least twice in your career you'll find yourself in the van of progress." Never a truer word was said, Jim,' said Fred Swellands. And so saying, Fred Swellands hawked and launched a wad of phlegm into the luxuriantly planted display of greenery beneath the trophy cabinet containing the shield that St Joseph of Cupertino's Under Elevens' football team had won for three years on the trot in the early seventies under Vinny Irlam, and which Mac had already brought back to St Joseph of Cupertino's on one occasion in the two years since Vinny Irlam had taken early retirement. 'Inspectorate? Hah! *Ex*-pectorate, more like!' said Fred Swellands, adding an expletive, and an apology: 'Pardon my French, Jim.'

'A-hem.' The younger priest, Fr Philip Newfield – the one who
was acting as secretary to the governors, usher for the candidates
to and from the interview room, and general factotum – Fr Philip
Newfield coughed politely, being mindful of the applicant's
apparent reticence in responding to the question that Fr Pavor had
put to him, though not at all mindful of the fact that failure to
access an applicant's references represented a singularly
significant abrogation of his gubernatorial responsibilities.

'What does my . . .?'

'What does your religion mean to you?' said Fr Pavor.

James Harney regarded these six strangers, their faces thrust
bleakly towards him like the prows of enemy shipping, their
features reflecting dully in the surface of the mahogany table-top:
Fr Thomas Pavor, the PP; Fr Philip Newfield, the younger priest
from the family of chain store clothiers; Laetitia Thirlwall, the JP
with her prissy mouth and a garnet ring with a stone the size of a
Victorian Penny Red; Hector Scoffington-Gordale, the local
authority inspector, sporting a mauve polka dot dicky-bow and an
M.A. (Oxon.); Reg Fawlee, the proprietor of the engineering
works on Hendham Vale, who had received considerable publicity
on Granada Television for his opposition to the introduction of the
metric system; and Alderman George Addlecock, the long-serving
councillor for the ward, who appeared to be giving his undivided
attention to the process of systematically, albeit discreetly, picking
his nose.

His religion – hell, decided Jim Harney – his pet dog Rastus
deserved more respect than this.

'Well, Father, I, er . . .' he heard himself mumble.

And the instant he heard the echo of his own voice in the
corners of the room a whole litany of words flowed freely into his
head, words resonant as surf on a shingle beach: Freedom and
Fair-Dealing, Honesty, Fraternity, Social Justice, and Truth . . .
My yoke is easy, and My burden light . . . Come to Me all ye who

labour and I will give you rest . . . For I am the Way, the Truth and . . .

In this same abstract form these words and others like them stopped short of his mouth, and he heard himself mutter something banal in the extreme which involved attending Sunday Mass and sending his two children to a Catholic school. Subsequently, he seemed to recall, the *Catholic Self-Servist* got a mention too. For Jim Harney was otherwise occupied whilst his lips were saying these things. He was watching, a bemused observer, as Aldernan Addlecock – his eyes unseeing like a fish on a slab – contrived to secrete his glutinous catch within the folds of his pocket handkerchief. The real words, the hard-won words, the words dredged from the depths of his experience and conviction – those words fell back again into the quiet waters of his consciousness: waters his God could tread, ever disdainful of testimony given for gain.

The woman was appointed – that same woman, the mother of three, who earlier in the evening amidst the camaraderie of the waiting room, had mentioned a Caribbean holiday planned for the last week in the month, a letter of support she had recently dispatched to a misanthrope at Westminster, and (immediately prior to a complete half minute's lull in the general conversation) an unspecified degree of consanguinity with the family of chain store clothiers. Smiling, Fr Thomas Pavor, shook hands with each of the three men in turn.

'Jaze!' one of them cursed with Celtic economy as the door of the presbytery swung shut behind them. 'An' it's divil the drop we'll get to drink, the time it is.'

Jim's wristwatch – the Avia inscribed "Jimmy – *toujours!*" that Stella had given him as a wedding present – said 10.41. The kids would have been in bed for a couple of hours now, and by the time he got home, supper would be ready. He left Mac and the Irish guy at the corner and, with them, a mental picture of St Joseph of Cupertino's Presbytery burning like the Reichstag, a Molotov cocktail flying ungainly as a raven from his own right hand. He began to hum to himself as he walked along; he hummed a nameless little tune without words, his footsteps resounding from the convent wall into the clear night air. He thought there'd be a frost before morning. He wondered briefly whether he'd have time to decorate the hall, stairs and landing before the twenty-fifth or whether he had better put it off until the half-term break in the New Year.

The Alliance Inn, corner of Kate Street/Rochdale Road, 1968

6

Life

Life, said the allegorist,
is like
a spent match you find in the street
when you desperately need a light.
It has a certain length,
of course,
but it's bland and pale
and featureless all the way through.

A man, said the visionary,
of substance
used that match – and he got a boxful.
And when he's used up his
average contents forty-eight,
he'll go straight out
and buy another box.

So, pull, said the pragmatist,
your finger out,
place your shoulder and nose to the etcetera.
Then one of these days
you'll be able to approach this man of substance
and ask him for a light.

Alternatively, said the fatalist,
you could always give up smoking.

7

COLORADO

To Smacker Rooney, *Moolah*, the *Daily Mess*

Sir,

Ref: Football Pool Collectors

You are, of course, quite correct in saying (*Moolah*, 20 September) that a football pools collector is the agent of his customer, not the pools company, although, as a former pools collector myself, I would maintain that the majority of pools collectors are scrupulously honest. But even if they were not, there remain two safeguards that protect the public from long-term fraud.

In the first place, if a collector does a bunk with the stakes, there is no danger the pools company is going to give him a fresh supply of coupons so he may repeat the exercise. And secondly, quite apart from winning the jackpot, literally thousands of punters win smaller prizes week after week. This fact alone dictates that even selective deception will be short-lived.

You may object that this is no consolation in the short term, and that only the Post Office remains a safe bet. But it was a postal strike that taught me this lesson in the first place since it necessitated the distribution of the smaller prizes by the collector network in my area. And my own customers, whom I had previously thought to be quite mad because they never seemed to win so much as a sausage, were then seen to be merely reticent about mentioning the stunning frequency with which they managed to strike it at least marginally lucky.

Yours,
Byron Marlfield
Colorado TV, Manchester
21 September 1981

Smacker Rooney says: *If it's a safe bet you want, perm any two from three – Coloroll, Ferranti, Polly Peck.*

8

Time Off for Bad Behaviour

McClintock was perfectly all right until the Guildford Four were released, he got into the habit of saying in later years. It was not true though; it was very far from the truth. The truth was that McClintock had never been one hundred per cent all right since McKay had turned up, and that was all of fourteen years ago now. McClintock had never seen eye to eye with McKay from the start, and McKay had never got on with McClintock; and since McKay was the new Governor (new as of fourteen years ago, that is) and McClintock was just another prisoner (Prisoner 56/4852, to be exact), it had been a cast-iron certainty that McClintock would come off worse.

And he had.

McClintock had come off worse than any of the other three hundred and eighty-five prisoners in the joint – that is, three hundred and eighty-five if you counted the screws and ancillary staff as prisoners, which they were in a way, because every last one of them was tied to HMP Joburg, as McClintock had taken to calling the joint in 1980, five years into his term.

Of course, McClintock had actually done seven years by then, but McClintock counted the arrival of McKay as the beginning of his term. In 1980, then, McClintock had been five years into his term by his own reckoning; and towards the end of 1989, he had done nine years more, nearly fourteen years in all.

It had not been easy for McClintock. The immediate and substantial loss of privileges decreed by McKay on arriving at HMP Joburg McClintock had just had to get used to, and he had. It had taken him some time to get used to this, of course, two or three years maybe. But, come, the winter of '78-'79, McClintock had become quite accustomed to being just another number, and he no longer lost sleep about it at night.

Water off a duck's back. Hah!

But it had been considerably harder – no, it had been well nigh impossible to become inured to McKay's constant carping criticism: the Chinese water torture of McClintock's waking hours – and consequently, McClintock's tobacco ration continued to receive a bit of a bashing even to this day.

Very irritating too was McKay's habit of addressing McClintock, not by his Christian name, but by his surname complete with the hyphenated pre-fix 'Mis-ter'. Thus: 'Mis-ter McClintock!' It would have been nice, thought McClintock, to be called 'Chrys' every once in a while even by Salieri McKay's pursed lips. Never mind the Chrysogonus. (McClintock never used his Sunday name himself – it made him squirm in much the same way it would have made him squirm if someone had referred to a Riley's Toffee Roll as a sweetmeat.) Yes, 'Chrys' would have been nice to hear every once in a while. On occasion, it might have substituted for the word 'please', itself a commodity in very short supply in the joint. Heck, McClintock would have much preferred – thought McClintock in the temporary seclusion of his prison cell whilst his thirty-two cell mates (no thirty-one today: Casio was laid up with rubella), whilst his thirty-one cell mates were out on the exercise yard – McClintock would have much preferred, he thought, to hear even the impersonal 'Prisoner 56/4852' rather than the ultra impersonal 'Mis-ter McClintock' on a day-to-day basis.

'I am a person,' McClintock reminded his prison cell, temporarily empty apart from himself and, therefore, quiet. 'I am a person,' McClintock told his prison cell.

McClintock's prison cell did not demur. McClintock's prison cell was so quiet as to be silent, save for the drumming noise made by McClintock's fingerstips on the arm of his chair.

'Oh, tha's okay, buddy!' McClintock, in Sean Connery mode, was eager to put his prison cell at its ease. 'Tha's okay! At least ye didn'y call me Mis-ter McClintock.'

Yes, and that was another thing while he was about it, thought McClintock. So, McClintock said to his prison cell: 'McKay's not fair to you either, buddy.'

Thirty-two prisoners to one cell – thirty-six on occasion: it was worse than *Midnight Express* in there at times with everyone belching and farting and breathing sour milk, so the window had to be kept wide open and, even wide open, it still wasn't much. It was a good job he could fight them all, thought McClintock – hey, with one hand tied behind his back too!

Hey, that McClintock, they said, he was the boy on this landing.

'Luke, you's sho' one mean son of a gun!' McClintock told his prison cell in George Kennedy mode, circa 1967.

McClintock's cell did not doubt it.

Sure, way back in – oh, when was it now? '73? '74? No. It was no good. McClintock had lost track of those early days. Hell, he hadn't even begun to keep count till McKay had turned up in the January of '76. But in the early days (McClintock rising, went across to the wall of his prison cell immediately behind the spot where he had been sitting, having a smoke, and tossing four lighted cigarette butts an hour out the window, hoping they'd maybe burn somebody's coat out on the exercise yard), sure, back in the early days he'd had to hit one or two of them with a stick. Till they got the message, that is. But they got the message, those guys. Bimberg . . . Sparky Ivanovitch . . . Jarowolski, Cameron, Johnny Klimt, Farquarson, O'Connell. Tough guys, great guys, but they got the message all right – well, the way McClintock put it to them, they did. Hey, and they passed that message right on down the line to those who came after them: Romanoff and Steve Burton, Carl Schmidt, Llewellyn, Bugsy Harrison. Great guys, wonderful guys, every one o' them – and, eventually (yeah, way back in '75, this was) McClintock had been able to put that stick of his away for good.

McClintock had really rubbed it in with that stick of his. Yeah, one day McClintock had taken that mother and had broken it in four in front of them. Thirty-four cons were in there that day, apart from McClintock himself, and McClintock had taken those four broken pieces of bamboo and thrown them out the same window through which he was now flicking four lighted cigarette butts an hour. Let 'em have 'em as souvenirs, McClintock could remember thinking at the time: They ain't none of them pieces big enough to do no damage to ol' McClintock. Hell, ain't none of them big enough they gonna do no damage to theirselves neither. And double negative be damned, thought McClintock.

43

Because it got that way that McClintock could stand there out on the exercise yard and, whenever he chose to do so, he could make those cons line up in front of him by means of the simple expedient of fixing the weakest one amongst them with his eyes – Lee Marvin-hard, Chief-Flew-Over-The-Cuckoo's-Nest-mute – and just staring at the sucker.

Hey, and in the snow . . . in the snow, that time, the one and only time McKay had let them out in it in – ah never mind when it was now, way back in history – the one and only time McKay had let the whole prison population out on the exercise yard when it was snowing real hard and three hundred and sixty cons had made with the snowballs. Even so, they let ol' McClintock walk from the Big House wall to the perimeter fence and back again without so much as a snowflake alighting upon his person apart from those the Good Lord was scattering like largesse from an overcast sky. Oh, they jossed him those guys, yeah, they jossed him. McClintock could take a joke, but he would only take it so far. It had been the look in his eyes that had told them to, 'Hey, maybe hold off, if you know what's good for you, son: Ah don't really think so, laddie, do you? No, maybe not the best idea you ever had in your life.' Yeah, that first (and last: the one and only) time on the exercise yard in the snow when the cons had plastered McKay with the stuff so her eyes were like – well, McKay's eyes were exactly like what Michael Caine said Ian Hendry's eyes were like at the races in *Get Carter*; and then nothing much could be done about it anyway, apart from McKay's imposing a permanent ban on any further sorties when it was snowing.

Oh, those guys! Collosimo . . . Jimmy Westbrook who lost his shirt at Sharston Baths, Stebulis who fell in four foot six with his clothes on, Chad Ireton (Chadderton, as they called him) who ran The Saddleback, the cross-country race, in his duffel coat – and won! Long gone now, the lot of them – Chad Ireton to an early grave, the poor sod, OD-ing on some shite he was into.

McClintock took the board from the wall and rested it on the floor and spun it round to reveal its obverse side. He took a stick of chalk in his hand and added a single chalk mark, one centimetre long, to the four chalk marks he had added earlier that week to the two thousand eight hundred chalk marks he had amassed in the fourteen years since McKay had turned up.

'My name is writ in water,' McClintock told the board from some half-remembered reading of long ago as he settled it back in its allotted position on the wall with the tally of his days hidden from view.

McClintock had stopped reading ten years before: reading for pleasure took a certain composure of mind, a quality McClintock had not been able to lay claim to for two thousand days and more.

'My name,' McClintock essayed again, the board appearing somewhat non-commital. 'My name is two thousand chalk marks on your backside . . . No, *up* your backside, pal!' muttered McClintock, though to himself now. Because at that moment, with thirty-two cons (thirty-one rather: Casio was laid up with rubella) filing back into McClintock's prison cell, McClintock felt more inclined towards the prosaic than the poetic.

Surely thirty-two cons to a cell (thirty-six on occasion) was frowned upon by the Home Office. Maybe he should have posted a complaint. But to whom? To whom could McClintock have made his complaint? Who was there in McClintock's hell on earth who would be interested enough to listen, never mind do something about it? Nobody at the Home Office, certainly. The kin Home Office had appointed Salieri Mc-bastard-McKay in the first place, for God's sake. No, no. Not for God's sake. Yes . . . yes, definitely for God's sake.

McClintock began to hum to himself the tune of a hymn that Fr Richard Bellis, the prison chaplain, sometimes used in the chapel. McClintock began to hum the tune to himself, and then to sing it under his breath as thirty-one cons belched and farted and breathed sour milk in a single prison cell – hey, and sniggered too today, hearing, Salieri McKay shrieking at some poor con out on the landing.

'My Go-od . . . ha-ates . . . me-e,' sang McClintock *sotto voce*. 'His ha-ate . . . will ne-e-ver end . . .'

Even so, McClintock felt he was overstating the case somewhat, though in the matter of subject rather than predicate. For there was no God, thought McClintock: there was no God because only last week McClintock had overheard the prison chaplain, the saintly Fr Richard Bellis, declare that Salieri McKay was 'the most thorough going professional' he had ever met. Therefore, there was no God.

'56/4852, reporting, *sah!*' McClintock had snapped on one (to him) memorable occasion, coming smartly to attention and saluting when Salieri McKay had cavilled over the precise positioning of the box in the gymnasium. But it had been more than the actual words McClintock spat out that had got to McKay – there had been an edge to McClintock's voice, an insubordinate tone that McClintock had been momentarily unable to subdue. What year had that been, McClintock wondered. How much porridge had he done by then? Seven years, ten? Was that before or after his oppo, Franny Quelch, got over the wall and away free?'

'Oh, what's the matter, Mis-ter McClintock?' McKay had said, rounding on him and fixing him with those grey/blue eyes of hers that seemed to be not so much a part of her face as imprisoned behind a mask that would not have been out of place on stage in a Greek tragedy. 'Is it that you can't take criticism, Mis-ter McClintock?'

'Not when it's the only effin' thing on offer, *sah!*'

Oh, trust him! Trust *him!* Yeah, McClintock only had to go and say it, thereby earning himself a stony silence for a fortnight and an adverse report (he was later to learn from his friend in Calderdale) clandestinely entered on his personal record at the Home Office.

Still, one thing that could be said in McClintock's favour (even in the days of his deepest disillusionment in the joint) was that McClintock had very early on come to realise that he knew how to do his time. And this is precisely what McClintock meant when he got into the habit of saying in later years that he was perfectly all right until the Guildford Four got out – even though McClintock was not all right, and had not been perfectly so for some fourteen years or more. But at some time or other, in that great long ago when reading had been McClintock's favourite form of relaxation and escape, McClintock could remember reading somewhere that if you can't do the time, you shouldn't do the crime. And this was precisely what McClintock prided himself on: he *could* do the time. Hell, he'd *done* the time (fourteen years of it so far), he could do all the time they threw at him. Because McClintock . . . well, McClintock was a lifer; and that's all there was to it.

Those guys: Ivanovitch, Collosimo, Steve Burton – even Franny Quelch, when it came right down to it: they'd done a stretch, sure, but then they'd gone on their way. They'd been sprung, released, sent forth into the world with a cheery godspeed. Only McClintock the Lifer remained: doing time McClintock knew how to do, within a prison population that changed from day to day, from month to month, and certainly, from year to year, inside this prison cell of his with its annual turnover of 30-plus cons (31 today with Casio laid up with rubella), and as many as 36 at times – a constant prison turnover except for McClintock the Lifer, doing time McClintock knew how to do. Hey, doing all the time McKay and them bastards at the Home Office could throw at him.

Routine helped, of course, a routine that suited McClintock's personal needs, and from year eight onwards McClintock had worked assiduously at his routine. From year eight onwards too McClintock had begun to withdraw into himself, gathering his strength about him – head down, chin tucked in, arms into the torso, fists clenched, elbows into the hip, sideways on, crouched, well-balanced on his feet, springy – in the defensive stance of the boxer who . . . will hit *out* if necessary . . . *No* . . . you do *not* . . . hit *me* . . . with *impunity!*

First to go was the sport – football, swimming team, cricket, athletics, cross country, gymnastics. Let McKay sort it out, if she could – gobshite, Madame Mwa Mem Salieri Mc-bastard-McKay! Quiz team, sack it; guitar, rack it; volunteering for anything without extra tobacco ration right there on the barrel head, pack it in, *absolument*. Thus, did McClintock the Lifer become McClintock the Pressed Man, attuned to his personal needs alone – to getting through the day, to getting through the week, the year, to survival, to eventual escape from this hell hole in seven years time when he'd be sixty-two years of age. Ah, yes! There were just seven years to go now before McClintock would be free – seven more years before McClintock would be beyond these prison walls with Marie and the kids and the grandkids where he knew he belonged.

McClintock's routine was rooted in personal cleanliness. He had no need of press-ups, sit-ups, or any other keep-fit method of survival. McClintock knew he could do the time. There was no question about it. But McClintock knew too that he mustn't weaken, that he must remain alert, that he must keep within his grasp that stark, focused, front-of-the-head determination to do the time and then get out. Hence, McClintock adopted a simple formula he had learned in that bibliophiliac long ago to the effect that, with a view to achieving alertness of mind, the poet John Keats would put on a clean shirt. So, at regular intervals, McClintock himself would put on a clean shirt, and he would prepare himself too with extensive ablutions prior to selecting that shirt.

Home leave helped him here. Yeah, there was that, of course. At least it was an open prison, and McClintock was permitted to go home at night and at the weekends, and he was, from time to time, granted extended leave of absence away from the joint, though only at those times when McKay herself was not there.

So, McClintock showered daily, shaved, and – Fybogel being an integral part of his ablutions, or a dozen satsumas in season – beshat himself each night in the privacy of his en suite bathroom and loo. He cleaned his teeth twice, gargled with Listerine, ear-pokered (cotton buds) his ears, paid special attention to his toenails and feet, shone his shoes on a broadsheet ready for morning prior to putting out the milk bottles each night and, on Mondays, the dustbin too.

Having arisen an hour before Marie in the morning, McClintock would shower again, dry shave sparingly and where necessary, evacuate his bowels if he could, wash his hands once more in the event of this, clean his teeth (twice), gargle with Listerine, smack his face with the *Insensé* aftershave Marie had bought him last Christmas but which could never holiday with him (McClintock distrusting its twist, as opposed to, screw top), roller deodorise his underarms (Vaseline branded), John Donne one of five clean cotton shirts of a Keatsian white (Rael Brook) that awaited him within his wardrobe, do up a Viyella tie (striped, and one of five: red/black, green/black, blue/grey, beige/brown, blue/bluer), shrug on the slate grey suit jacket that went with the slate grey trousers he was already wearing (one of two matching pairs that went with the jacket: the trousers seemed to get all the wear these days), pick up the BMW car key-fob from the window ledge by the front door, kiss Marie goodbye, and set off to gaol once more in his Daytona yellow Ford Cortina Mk III or (from year four of his stretch) his Island blue British Leyland Marina 1.8 saloon.

Breaks, dinnertime, whenever he was not required out on the exercise yard, McClintock would keep to his cell with a sandwich and a flask from home, and read the paper. He ran the gamut of the dailies over the years: *Thames*, *Gruinard* (briefly), *Tellygraph*, *Mess*, no newspaper at all; and then back again, starting with the *Thames*, missing out the *Gruinard* and finishing up with nowt.

'Newspapers,' McLintock said to his prison cell one day, 'what have you got when you've got them?'

McClintock's cell said nothing as per usual, and for once McClintock's cell was right.

Then, rising from his repast (perm any two from ten: corned beef/white bread, cheddar cheese/brown, ham/wholemeal, beef/muffin, chicken/bagel – invariably accompanied by a packet of Golden Wonder Salt and Vinegar crisps, and followed by a Blue Riband biscuit and a flask of Joe Lyons' coffee) McClintock would proceed to the washroom behind the podium in the assembly hall. (Even under Salieri McKay trusties were permitted to use this.) In all likelihood McClintock's Fybogel intake would not be in evidence until the early evening, so McClintock would strip off his shirt and tie, buff his shoes with a Boston Max shoe shine pad, and make systematic use of a variety of ablutionary condiments that came to hand because McClintock had previously arranged that they should be available to come to hand – a tablet of Imperial Leather soap (hands, arms, armpits, face, ears, and neck), Gillette Blue II disposable razor (dry shave unless more drastic action were deemed necessary), Colgate toothpaste (twice), Wilko Fresh Mint mouthwash (a third the price of Listerine, and more palatable), Imperial Leather Classic aftershave (a veteran – like McClintock himself – of Sorrento, Cattolica, the Algarve, Almeria; and the Costas Blanca, Brava and del Sol: having a screw top, it holidayed with him too), Palmolive underarm spray, shirt on, tie affixed in good order, suit jacket brushed down with the clothes brush that holidayed with him too, Denman-brushed hair, ready for inaction . . .

What the hell was that doing there?

A Gale's honey pot, long since bereft of honey and label, now fifty percent filled (it was *filled* rather than *emptied*, McClintock being the one who had fifty per cent filled it) with inky black water (which had been of North West Water Board clarity when McClintock had fifty per cent filled it), and containing the one and a half inch Hamilton paint brush that McClintock had parked up in it the previous evening too.

Of course!

McClintock had been caught short when the Fybogel kicked in after the lads had gone off home at five o'clock. He had meant to tip the dirty water down the sink but had forgotten about it. He did this now (tipped it), washed the honey pot out, cleaned the paint brush. Within five minutes McClintock was banged up back in his cell again.

The scenery that had necessitated the one and a half inch Hamilton paint brush, the Gale's honey pot partially filled with water, and a tin of Macpherson's matt black emulsion paint (all items now safely back under lock and key in McClintock's stock cupboard) – the scenery that had necessitated all this represented the last vestige of that personal initiative-cum-proactivity that McClintock had always prided himself on before it was rendered of no account on the arrival of Salieri McKay. The scenery McClintock had clung to, in principle as opposed to physically, though very much as a dying man might cling to a crucifix, to his girl's photograph, or to his last monthly statement from the Avon & Test Building Society sharing an envelope with a notice to the effect that, in the event of a notified decease, the account would be frozen. And the reason why McClintock had clung to his responsibility for the scenery was for the sake of the Penal Battalion – or rather for the sake of a succession of Penal Battalions: fourteen or fifteen Penal Battalions to be more precise. Because, it was with the assistance of the various Penal Battalions down the years, that McClintock had painted the scenery for fifteen summer shows and seventeen Christmas nativity plays, the seventeenth nativity scene having been completed the previous night.

Joseph, Oliver, Superstar, Bugsy Malone, Treasure Island, Aladdin, Puss in Boots, Cinderella – you name it: McClintock and one or other of the Penal Battalions had painted the scenery for them all. McClintock had forgotten some of the shows, two or three maybe, the others being the same shows revisited (*Joseph and the Amazing Technicolor Dreamcoat* having been done to death on three separate occasions for reasons of apposite nomenclature). And last night McClintock and this year's Penal Battalion, the eleven kids who had been barred from Salieri McKay's rehearsals on account of bad behaviour (bad behaviour on the part of McKay or of the kids, McClintock never had been able to determine) had daubed a backdrop Bethlehem of sugar cube houses with navy blue squared windows, a navy blue sky, a single giant, yellow star, and three side screens on which were depicted a donkey, a cow, a handful of sheep, plus – on the obverse sides (which would be spun around at the interval to reveal) a brace of camels and a palamino, this last rearing on its hind legs, in fright presumably, on account of the unaccustomed smell of the orient which had been borne hither from the costume cupboard along with make-believe gifts of gold, frankincense, and myrrh.

It was usually lads whom McClintock would press into service in the Penal Battalion (they were all lads this year), a *salon des refusés* in which *mesdemoiselles* had ever been thin on the ground. Still, there had been one or two lasses in the past – Rachel Rishworth who was the second cock of the school in McClintock's tenth year of imprisonment . . . Wanda Mendoza of whom it had been said by someone from the Remedial Service (Amazulu or

51

Khan or Prognosis, or whatever her name was) that Wanda Mendoza was the girl who 'put the *ug* in *ugly*'. (Wanda was also a girl, McClintock had noticed, who was an enthusiastic colourist when McClintock would Rolf Harris an apposite line drawing, and the Penal Battalion would be called upon to do the colouring in.) Yes, and stumpy Antoinette Chang whom that same wag from the Remedial Service (or was that Myxyptlk in Special Needs?) had averred was 'the girl who put the malaise in Malaysia', Malaysia being Antoinette's country of origin. (Yet again McClintock would have disagreed; to McClintock's way of thinking, Antoinette Chang's chief failing was that she had presumed to transmit that malaise to U.K. plc.) But this year McClintock's Penal Battalion consisted entirely of boys: Bimberg the Younger, Casio the Youngest, Romanoff the son of Romanoff, Balanciaga the Cousin, Jarowolski the Second Generation, Gibson the Umpteenth. Would they never learn, these lads? Well, yes, they *would* – when they were of a mind to do so, and when they were able to work unhindered by Salieri McKay's high-pitched screech, which, being reminiscent perhaps of the origins of their forebears in the primeval jungle, tended to incline them towards re-visiting it.

McClintock smiled. McClintock's prison cell was unused to this: McClintock's prison cell remonstrated with him via a knocking at the door. Or was it applause perhaps, wondered McClintock in that brief moment before Mavis Scoberry entered, smiling apologetically, and advanced on McClintock's desk in her dinner supervisor's blue gingham tabard that would be left behind her for good, come Christmas, when she left to take up a new posting at Goodall's baker's shop.

'Mr McClintock?'

An improvement on Mis-ter McClintock anyway, thought Prisoner 56/4852.

'Now, Mavis, how long have we known each other? Call me Chrys, please.'

'It just seems funny,' said Mavis Scoberry.

'Oh, it's funny all right. You don't know the half of it.'

Mavis Scoberry's face was a blank.

'What it's short for, I mean.'

'Christopher?'

''Fraid not, but I'd consider it an act of mercy if you'd go right on thinking that.'

Mavis Scoberry looked distinctly uncomfortable.

'I'm kidding, Mavis. Take no notice of me. The mind goes numb after a while, sitting here on your todd, reading about shawls of fish, prides of loins, and flooks of sheep . . .'

Mavis Scoberry relaxed visibly, though not at all completely. 'I was, er, I was wond'rin' if you'd do somethin' for me, Mr McClintock.'

'Sure, if I can,' McClintock ventured another smile.

McClintock's cell registered another objection: the radiators rattled briefly.

'With you bein' the deputy and that.'

McClintock continued to smile encouragement. Aye, and head bottle washer too, he thought. This was McClintock's third smile of the day. McClintock's cell took it on the chin.

Ah, yes, Mavis – McClintock, continuing to smile, failed to say – Deputy I am indeed, though it's Deputy-effin'-Dawg more like, if you ask me. Yep, Fred Swellands appointed me back in – well, you weren't around at the time, Mavis – back in '73. Yeah, Vinny Irlam had taken early retirement with his missis being ill – on her last legs as it happened, '74 -ish Carmelita died. And Marie, my Marie: well, you met Marie when we did Puss In Boots, Mavis – fetched the little uns with her. She'd just had our youngest the April before. Fifteen she is now, our Michele. Anyway, Fred Swellands took me on as deputy, and we had two great years together, Fred and me, till Sal. . . . well, till Mrs McKay . . . Well, yes – McClintock, smiling, continued to leave these things unsaid – that is one thing we do have in common, me and her . . . Mrs McKay – with her being deputy here immediately before Vinny Irlam, before she went for promotion to . . . Yeah, All Vandals and Wreckers – I know, Mavis? My pal out in the sticks, Calderdale, he loves that . . . Fuggin' Group 6 deputy headship at All Vandals and Wreckers, as you call it, Mavis – McClintock continuing to think but failing to say, smiled on. Not that McKay was Fred Swellands' appointment here at St Joey's, you know. Oh, she was appointed in Fred's time all right, but not by Fred Swellands is what I mean. Oh no, Mavis, that was Fr Earwig's doing, Fr Elrick . . . Fr Elrick appointed McKay as deputy. Yeah, in fact, Fred Swellands was so pissed off with the way things were going in the interviews, he went and sat in with the candidates, leaving the Governors to make the appointment without him. Or so I'm told. Hah! Talk about washing your hands of something without using a bowl of water! And, in retrospect, of course, Fred Swellands did for me, doing that, Mavis . . . Sitting in with the candidates like that. Oh, it was before my time, of course, but McKay knew Fred had snubbed her, didn't she? And she knew he did no such thing when I was appointed. See, I was Fred Swellands' appointment as deputy, Mavis. Yeah, Took us out for a few Jameson's at the North Parade after the interview too. Flippin' Ay-Tees, if you don't mind, Mavis. Didn't get home till after midnight. Marie was going frantic. Still, you only live once, eh? Well, no, that's not quite true, Mavis; you only live for a couple of years, as it happens. I mean, I had two fabulous years with Fred Swellands. Had another good year when McKay took secondment: B.Phil (Flower Arrangement) or some damned silly thing, Shrilly Shouting, maybe. Much good it did me though. Getting glowing reports all round, till I found out on the Q.T. (mate of mine works in Calderdale, where I applied for St Yonner's-In-The-Back-Of-Beyond one time) that my bloody Home Office record had been got at. Saw it with my own eyes, Mavis. Yeah! Hey, how about this, Mavis? You'll remember it: you were here then. Let's see, you came – see if I'm right? You came '80. Right? I was made up to acting head '82. Yeah, that's right. You girls did a marvellous job sorting out the scran for the kids' party after we held the Inter-Schools Concert in the spring that year. Same year we had Keep Britain Tidy, a football team that won the Under 11s' Trophy, a cricket team, quiz team with a cup, swimming team with medals – swimming gala in the summer, athletics team, two parents' evenings, a Christmas concert, summer show . . . Your Ian was the Marquis of Carabas, if I remember rightly. No, that was your Betty's lad, wasn't it? Your Ian was Puss. Hey, remember that line of his, Mavis?

'Ee, Cyril, lad, tha's coom on grand like summat supersonic –
'Let's call in at the North Parade an' have a gin an' tonic?'
Oh, fu . . . crying out loud. Mavis! – McClintock, smiling,
continued not to say. We were really busy that year McKay was in
Scunthorpe or wherever they do certificatable or certifiable Flower
Arranging. We had a full rota anyway. Proactive Pete, you know
me, Mavis. Well, as you used to know me, that is. I mean, what
the hell are they doing down the Home Office – okay, the
Education Offices, letting a comment like that get on my record
that's only been got at by Salieri McKay in cahoots with Mr
Hector Scoffington-Gumdrop, MA (Oxon.) who appointed her?
"Satisfactory." I ask you, Mavis? You ever feinted with damp
praise, Mavis? Tell you, I wanted to take that Scottish Primary
Maths Group Scheme I pioneered in this fair city of ours and ram
it up you-know-whose Salierian and you-know-whose Oxonian
back passages, Mavis. But guess what I done instead, Mavis.
Yeah, "done", Mavis, fuck 'em! (As you so politely don't put it
with knobs on, Mavis.) Voila, ten years on – fourteen years on
from ground zero: Prisoner 56/4852, McClintock, Cell Block 4M,
HMP Joberg: St Joseph of Cupertino's RC Primary School (a
Catholic, though not, a Christian school, because 'Christian is,' as
my pal Franny Quelch used to say, 'as Christian does!'). Yep,
Prisoner 56/4852 McClintock, that's me, Mavis, with seven years
to do until he's sixty-two and can go home to Marie and the kids
and the grandkids on the threshold of the new millennium. Go on,
guess what I done instead, Mavis? I done time, Mavis. Yeah,
that's what I done, Mavis. I done time. And they didn't break me,
did they, Mavis? You'll be the judge of that, won't you?
McClintock done his time, McClintock done all the time the
bastards threw at him. Yeah, "done", Mavis. Fuck 'em, as you
seem to be getting in the habit of so politely not putting it with
knobs on and a cherry on top.

The foregoing is what McClintock most definitely did not
say; what follows is what Mavis Scoberry did:

'Mr McClintock, they won't gi' me no money wi' me only
doin' nine years.'

'Pardon?'

'Me gratuity. They give you £20 for every year you've done. But you gotta do ten years minimum, else you get nowt. I was wonderin' if . . .'

'You're leaving us?'

'Surely, you knew that, Mr McClintock?'

'Yes . . . yes, of course I did,' said McClintock quickly. 'I'm sorry, Mavis. I was miles away.'

There had been a bit of bad feeling for some time between Mavis Scoberry and Ethel Birkdale, both of them dinner supervisors, though the precise details of the disagreement eluded McClintock for the moment. Not that the details mattered, except to Mavis Scoberry and Ethel Birkdale, of course. What really mattered was that the disagreement had festered over two school terms, was common knowledge to everyone in the school except the kids, had not been sorted by Salieri McKay, and had developed into a full scale row in which the dinner ladies and supervisors were now divided into two tabarded armies with the cook acting as ringmaster with rolling-pin to hand.

'I was wond'rin' if you'd maybe have a word wi' someone at the offices for me. You must know somebody there.'

Mr Scoffington-Effin'-Gumdrop, MA (Oxon.), McClintock now failed to say. McClintock said: 'What about, Mrs McKay? Have you asked, Mrs McKay?'

Mavis Scoberry shrugged noncommittally, and in so doing gave McClintock an answer to his question.

Salieri McKay was on – what? Well, let's for the sake of the argument say £20,000 p.a. in round figures in 1980s' money, thought McClintock. So, £20,000 p.a. divided by two, equals a pension entitlement of £10,000 p.a., provided McKay had forty years in. So, when she retired Salieri McKay would receive an index-related annual pension equivalent to forty eightieths of her final salary, plus she'd get a lump sum of £30,000, all of this entitlement being funded by a 6 per cent superannuation contribution from her salary over forty years of pensionable service.

Very serviceable, indeed!

Well, okay – thought McClintock – so Mavis Scoberry had

made no pension contributions whatsoever; neither did she have forty years service in, and, subsequent to bringing up five kids, she had worked part-time for the past nine years at the most . . . But the Home Office was cribbing about what? A measly £180 quid? – or whatever might be deemed to be the pro rata rate over nine years that, according to Home Office rules, must be ten years of service before Mavis Scoberry would get so much as a carrot? McClintock felt his jowls flush with anger, the hairs across his neck and shoulder blades stand on end. It was all he could do to prevent himself crying out:

'Woe to you Pharisees! You love the front seats in the synagogues and greetings in the market place . . . You are like hidden tombs over which men walk unaware . . . Woe to you! You load men with oppressive burdens and do not lift a finger to help them . . . You have taken away the key of knowledge. You have not entered yourselves and those who were entering you have hindered . . .'

Whoa, steady on, boy! McClintock cautioned himself. You've got seven years to do yet: you'll never make it at this rate!

The telephone calls McClintock made to the Home Office (as McClintock termed the Education Offices in those days) had to be made when the coast was clear. (McKay had adjourned to a bistro called Shysters off the M61 at Westhoughton where a Mr Cholmondely-Foetid – or so McClintock had understood him to say when he'd telephoned the school – a publisher of schoolbooks with the Kindercon Group, seemed eager to discuss McKay's proposed manual on Flower Arranging for the Under-Fives, and treat her to lunch.) And thankfully, Schools Eight, the section which dealt with dinner ladies, supervisors and ancillary staff appeared to be staffed by personnel who did not regard themselves as a cut above ordinary mortals, unlike Schools Nine, which his friend in Calderdale said was German for: 'The answer's no, now what's the question?' Furthermore, the young woman who took his call at NUPE was an absolute charmer. McClintock put the story to them like this:

Naturally, Mavis Scoberry could not remain anonymous, but once McClintock had assured both parties that he was telephoning at her behest, that he did not intend to discuss her private business with either party other than to possit her case and leave it with them – once he had done this, McClintock relayed the details of the case to them in terms that were as measured as they were circumspect.

No gratuity, said McClintock, was due to Mavis Scoberry under current regulations. There could be absolutely no argument about that. But Mavis Scoberry had given loyal service to the Authority over some nine years, and the qualifying additional year would almost certainly have been done, had the decision not been taken out of her hands, so to speak. What could be said to have begun as a slight contretemps between two colleagues had got a little out of hand – indeed, it had got out of hand to such an extent that it might be felt by those who exercised jurisdiction in these matters that Mavis Scoberry might be considered to be temporarily unwell since, all things being equal, it might be thought unusual, to say the least, for an employee who might expect a gratuity of £200 to be forthcoming in twelve months time to disqualify herself by prior resignation from a post in which she had previously been perfectly happy and to which she had always seemed to be eminently suited.

Once upon a time, said McClintock, he had heard of another education authority (Calderdale, according to McClintock's pal) where a native Irishman with some sixteen years service with that authority had never again returned to English soil subsequent to one particular summer recess. Accordingly, the powers-that-be had decided to award the man his full superannuable rights, believing that his non-return to his place of employ, without due notice, might tend to suggest he was unwell. McClintock had then expressed his gratitude for a sympathetic ear (well, two ears actually, though McClintock had not addressed them in tandem; nor did he now), and he concluded by leaving the matter in their capable hands, both conciliar and unionist.

The upshot was that Mavis Scoberry was granted a gratuity of £180 – or so McClintock heard on the grapevine. Because never to this day has he heard the news from Mavis Scoberry herself; and what follows may well be the reason why. For there remains the distinct possibility that Mavis Scoberry may not have been best pleased with McClintock's handling of the situation, a thought which occurred to McClintock subsequent to a telephone conversation – a rudely interrupted telephone conversation! – that McClintock had with Mavis Scoberry's son, Ian, subsequent to his telephone conversations with the LEA and NUPE.

When the telephone rang at home that night McClintock was studying with interest the teachers' pensions entitlement booklet that Marie had rooted out for him prior to taking the kids to her mother's. He let the telephone ring three times and then lifted the receiver.

Ian Scoberry's manner, initially conversational (their mutual point of reference being Ian's progress at the high school and sixth form college since he had passed beyond the scope of McClintock's tutelage together with what had more recently transpired regarding the two contacts that McClintock had made on his mother's behalf earlier in the day), Ian Scoberry's manner had become decidedly stilted as the details of McClintock's earlier telephone conversations were made clear to him. Mrs Scoberry's case had been fully explained to the people whose business it was to deal with such matters; what happened now was entirely up to them, explained McClintock. Regarding what he himself had said to those officials, McClintock told Ian Scoberry verbatim. And it was at this point that McClintock became aware of a decided chill in the atmosphere, Ian Scoberry's words becoming more careful, very formal, quite clipped.

What the hell was the matter with the lad? McClintock honestly felt that he had done everything he possibly could do for Mavis Scoberry short of pulling his tripes out and displaying them in Burton's window.

Then, as if in answer to what puzzled McClintock, Ian Scoberry told him exactly what the trouble was – and in such a way that McClintock knew beyond a shadow of a doubt that Mavis Scoberry was standing next to her son in their living-room at home.

'My mother, Mis-ter McClintock,' said Ian Scoberry in the instant before he cut McClintock off, 'my mother, Mis-ter

McClintock is not at all unwell. As a matter of fact, Mis-ter McClintock, my mother is in the very best of health.'

Rude health, presumably, thought McClintock. You insufferable little *prick!*

But there was, McClintock found, a bonus to be gleaned from the situation.

Because it was at this precise moment that it dawned on McClintock how he was going to do it! Oh, McClintock already knew *what* he was going to do – what he *had* to do. He had watched the Guildford Four on the street outside the Old Bailey on the early evening news on BBC1 – Gerry Conlan, his arms raised above his head, articulate and jubilant subsequent to their eventual triumph in the face of oppression; Paul Hill, whom the Kennedy family had taken to themselves – and the other two (photographs only) to whom more damage had been done than anybody in this great country of ours (hah!) could reasonably be expected to cope with. Four dupes of the State, a couple of brace to be immolated for the good of the System. If you can't do the time, McClintock reminded himself, then don't do the crime – but the Guildford Four had done the time and the Guildford Four had *not* done the crime. Even so, the Guildford Four were not doing time no more.

'And damn the double nuga . . . Damn the double negative.'

It dawned on McClintock that he had very nearly said *nugatory*, and it wasn't nugatory. No, it bloody-well wasn't nugatory. On two counts it wasn't nugatory. It wasn't bloody-well nugatory at all. And be damned to double negatives. Let's have it right, thought McClintock, what do niceties of architectural form matter if the building itself rests on a shaky foundation? Because McClintock had done the time too, and McClintock had *not* done the crime. Hey, what crime anyway? What crime was McClintock guilty of? Being handy as a scapegoat in the wrong place at the wrong time like the Guildford Four? And furthermore – thought McClintock – McClintock was still *doing* time! But not for no longer, no more. Well, not for much longer, no more. Double negative, treble negative, be damned. Because before very long McClintock was gonna be sprung.

By the time Ian Scoberry had telephoned him McClintock was already set on going over the wall. Reason: McClintock had learned from the booklet Marie had dug out for him that should he retire on grounds of ill-health, close on seven years would be added to his superannuable entitlement. So, there was no need to hang fire until the summer of 1996, nearly seven years in the future. If McClintock went over the wall right now, he'd do just fine. He'd have forty reckonable years of service in. So McClintock could be over the wall and away free, with a full pension in his sky. ('Sky rocket', that is, as Franny Quelch's brother-in-law would call it – the wonderful mellifluously-mouthy, arrogant Cockney git.)

Yeah, McClintock was gonna do a runner; and he'd do it right after Christmas. Because McClintock knew how he was going to do it now. Yep, just as soon as Ian Scoberry turned nasty – the insufferable little prick! – McClintock had known exactly how he was going to do it! Okay, so he'd have to wait until the first day back after the Christmas holiday before he acted. But, in a way, that made it even better, because it would leave Salieri McKay shorthanded at short notice, and she might have to get off her backside and take a class herself for once in her life. It was a pity about Oliver Hern, who was still on Red Book 2, thought McClintock, and Miranda Humesett, who couldn't even count under pressure. But it was time to put all that behind him now, thank God. Yeah, thank God, thought McClintock. At last it was time to act.

It would take some spunk, of course – well, in the American sense of the word anyway. But by all that was holy, McClintock was determined to have a stab at it. *Ah-ha-ha!* Oh, not a stab, McClintock! No, not a stab: McClintock was gonna have a go! Yeah, that was better. It would be a good Christmas this year too, a Christmas to look forward to, one of the best Christmases of McClintock's life – even counting the Christmases when McClintock was a kid and he would always get the thing he most wanted in all the world because he had a maiden aunt who never failed to make sure that he did.

Teachers' pay and teachers' workloads never have had a good press for the simple reason that everyone has been to school, and so everyone is an expert on educational matters – in much the same way as everyone who lives in a city and has walked down a city street knows exactly how to pave those streets and tarmacadam them and lay drains and services for the public utilities and set up traffic lights that work and paint yellow lines and direct traffic flow, and police them too.

Besides, it is a matter of simple arithmetic for anyone who has ever been to school that teachers have twenty-six weeks holiday a year and get double pay in the holidays, and – on the rare occasions when teachers are actually in school, they work from 9.00 am till 11.00 am, then have a half hour coffee break (with free milk), work from 11.30 am till 12 noon, then have two hours for dinner (and free dinners), work from 2.00 pm till 2.30 pm, then have a half hour coffee break (with more free milk), work from 3.00 pm till 4.00 pm (unless they teach in an infant school, of course, in which case they only work from 3.00 pm till 3.30 pm), and then they go off home and put their feet up and take it easy till it's time for bed. In other words, everyone in the UK knows that teachers work four hours a day at the most – which is just twenty hours a week, or a measly 520 hours per annum. Hey, and there's the rest of us working from 9 to 5, 7 days a week, 365 days a year. So that's nearly 3000 hours a year the rest of us have to work.

Bastard teachers! And they're always whingeing too!

So it was reassuring, indeed, when Kenneth Baker, the Thatcherite statesman and philanthropist, perfected a wonderful government scheme by means of which teachers in England and Wales have, since the mid-1980s, had to work five extra days a year for no extra pay.

Hey, quite right too!

The Baker Days (mark the name!) are still with us, and it is nothing short of scandalous that their original nomenclature has in some cases been lost to the public domain, denying due and proper recognition to the man who so gifted a debased profession. The

Baker Days (ah! you remembered!) are scattered amongst the various half-terms of the school year (either at the beginning or the end thereof), and on days such as these teachers in England and Wales are obliged to foregather in school bereft of kids (and, indeed, emolument) to discuss things, to prepare things – or to attend courses such as the vitally important topic which is under review in the assembly hall of St Joseph of Cupertino's RC Primary School on the morning of Monday 9 January, 1990 – namely, *Essential Flower Arrangement For the Under-Fives.*

The course is being presented by no less a personage than Mrs Sally R.E. McKay, B Phil. (FA), headteacher of St Joseph's, with Hector Scoffington-Gordale MA (Oxon.), the LEA Inspector, in the chair, whilst some seventy-two teachers and other interested parties are in attendance, quite a few of them taking notes, though Mrs Stella Harney appears to be the only one (bright floral displays being much in evidence) who has had the presence of mind to bring along with her a Kodak flash camera, the one that Jimmy has given her as a Christmas present.

At 11.21 am precisely – in fact, just as soon as those in attendance have taken their seats again after the scheduled coffee break, but before the general hubbub has died down – Mr Chrys McClintock, a member of St Joseph's staff, the deputy head of the school since 1973, excuses himself and, detaching himself from the other seventy-one people in the assembly hall, adjourns to the washroom behind the podium where he approaches his ablutions as is his wont.

McClintock doffs his coat, his shirt and tie; he buffs his shoes; washes his hands, arms, armpits, face, ears, and neck with a tablet of Imperial Leather soap; he cleans his teeth twice, swills his mouth with Wilko Fresh Mint for a full half minute; he slaps on Imperial Leather Classic aftershave; he uses Palmolive underarm spray with some abandon. And finally – fresh white shirt on, tie in place and tidily knotted – McClintock brushes his suit jacket, Denman brushes his hair . . .

R-R-R-R-R-R-R-R

Wha-what the kin hell was *that*?

R-R-R-R-R-R-R-R . . .

The racket which has arisen in an adjoining room confirms the fact that two men from Direct Works, who earlier this morning were blocking the entrance to the school car park with a Transit van with a ladder above it (on its roof) and a flat tyre below (o/s front), have now commenced attacking an adjacent breeze block wall with a Kango hammer. But, Kango-hammered racket notwithstanding, McClintock is finally ready . . . well, almost. Washed, deodorised, dry-shaven, coiffured, sweet-smelling, tidy and clean . . .

R-R-R-R-R-R-R . . .

McClintock unleashes The McClintock!

R-R-R-R-R-R-R . . .

McClintock un-zips it, unearths it – unsheaths the thing from his undergarments.

R-R-R-R-R-R-R . . .

Pendulous, if not pendulant . . .

R-R-R-R-R-R-R . . .

But clearly on view for those who have eyes to see it.

R-R-R-R-R-R-R . . .

Behold: The McClintock!

R-R-R-R-R-R-R . . .

McClintock's todger! *Voila!* McClintock's old man! Verily, courtesy of Ian Scoberry, son of Mavis Scoberry: prick – McClintock's prick!

R-R-R-R-R-R-R . . .

McClintock checks his reflection in the mirror above the sink.

"Gentlemen, please adjust your dress before leaving." McClintock recalls with wry amusement the sign that used to hang in the subterranean toilets beneath Piccadilly Gardens and Queen Victoria's stone-sculpted feet; McClintock smiles. Never a man to contravene convention, McClintock adjusts his dress: his tie – the green/black one, as it happens. McClintock's prick stays put, in full public (indeed, pubic) view.

'Who are these people?' McClintock (leaning forward and slightly red in the face) enquires of his reflection in the mirror above the sink in the washroom behind the stage. 'Who are these kin people?'

Then, turning, McClintock walks out of the washroom and into the rest of his life.

Two ramblers atop Malham Cove in Malhamdale in North Yorkshire – both Romanian booted, one in a blue and white Peter Storm cagoule, his companion in a lovat-coloured Goretex anorak, both bobble-hatted – two ramblers straddle the grykes of the limestone pavement, sure-footed above the clints, as they gaze towards the south and Aire Head Springs, a mile and a half distant along the line of Malham Beck, which issues from the foot of Malham Cove two hundred sheer feet below them. The man in the Peter Storm cagoule takes a snap of the scene with the Kodak flash camera he bought for his wife at Christmas and which, some eight months before this day, had caused a bit of a stir at Boots the Chemist when Stella Harney took it in complete with a roll of film for developing.

'Well, lads. There's good news and there's bad news,' Sergeant Don Jarvis of Greater Manchester Police had told the day shift on parade at Plant Hill Police Station when instructed to investigate the matter of one of the negatives which Mrs Stella Harney had handed in to Boots the Chemist for development. 'The good news is there's no need for a dawn raid on this one: it's not King Kong we're after, more like a chihuahua stood up on its hind legs. Kick up the arse'd bring it to its senses, you ask me. The bad news is it's some feller's got his dick out and we've got to find him before he catches chin-cough. God knows he'll not be harming any lady we know of, not unless disappointment can kill.'

The subject of the photograph to which Sergeant Jarvis was referring – now fully, and more appropriately clad in a Goretex anorak, backs away from the edge of Malham Cove and leads on to the Dry Valley that will take him and his companion through to Water Sinks and Malham Tarn.

His case had been easily explained to Sergeant Jarvis's men, particularly in view of the sick note from Doctor Stanegate that had been in his possession at the time. The only words he had thought to utter in his own defence were that it had been particularly cold in school on the day the photograph was taken because the men with the Kango hammer had turned the central heating off. Sergeant Jarvis' men had not pressed him to prove his point.

Some way into the Dry Valley above Malham Cove there is a cave. There is an echo, too, that reflects many a voice from Pennine Wayfarers who pass this way. Laughter, on the other hand – perhaps due to shortness of breath after the climb up the steps to the left-hand side of the Cove – is a much rarer phenomenon at this juncture. But there is laughter today, and from both men too. For today is a Monday, and it's the day the kids have gone back to school after the long summer break. As so often happens too, it is a sunny day after two weeks of torrential rain.

Blackley Library, corner of Blackley Park Road/Rochdale Road, 1958

66

9

The Headteacher's Ten Commandments
(A Lack of Principles for Principals)

1. Thou shalt take no class unto thyself during absence of staff lest thou shouldst sully thyself and betray thy high calling. [Revised Standard Version: Be a layabout.]

2. Thou shalt not frequent the yard at recess lest staff be scandalised and wouldst mutter amongst themselves, saying: 'Lo! this person is vulgar, and doth menial work just as we who are unworthy. [RSV: Be out of touch.]

3. Thou shalt keep to thine inner sanctum when thou canst discover no spurious errands to pursue across the face of the earth. [RSV: Be exclusive.]

4. Thou shalt go abroad amongst the peoples during the hours of daylight. Thus wilt thou amass thy credit one hundredfold with thy Father Who is in The Offices, and thy mileage sheet shalt yield a bountiful harvest even if thou canst not a JP be. [RSV: Be elusive.]

5. Thou shalt regard staff as pariah dogs which set up a discordant yelping if encouraged – demanding sops from thy table, even though they toil not as thou dost in the sweat of thy brow. [RSV: Be aloof.]

6. Thou shalt be as an avenging angel, smiting fearlessly to left and right, lest staff harbour feelings of job satisfaction. [RSV: Be a know-all.]

7. Thou shalt keep unto thyself all the audio-visual and technological idols staff would fain adore. [RSV: Be acquisitive.]

8. Thou shalt accept no suggestions from staff, for they are as sheep without understanding. Instead, let such suggestions come to fruition within thy noodle and after the passage of many seasons then mayst thou introduce them as the fruit of thine own deliberations. [RSV: Be a plagiarist.]

9. Thou shalt summon staff together each week without fail, and

when thou hast gathered them in the place where the waters meet and they imbibe the Ishmaelite beverage in copious draughts, then shalt thou speak swiftly and ceaselessly without remit. [RSV: Be a bore.]

10. Thou shalt have no abiding educational philosophy: thou shalt be as the shifting sands of the desert; yea, even as a rudderless ship. [RSV: Be unpredictable.]

Here endeth the lesson.

The Eight Phases of an Educational Initiative

1. 1999: 'Do it Thisaways!'
   – Hector Scoffington-Gordale, M. A. (Oxon.)

2. 2000: 'Do it Thataways!'
   – Hector Scoffington-Gordale, M. A. (Oxon.)

3. 2001: 'Thiswaways? Thataways?' Just get it done!'
   – Hector Scoffington-Gordale, M. A. (Oxon.)

4. 2002: 'Thisaways? Thataways? *Preposterous*!'
   – HM Chief Inspector of Schools, M.A. (Cantab.).

5. 2003: Baker Days throughout the LEA are devoted exclusively to the eradication of Thisaways and Thataways Methodologies.

6. 2004: ditto

7. 2005: ditto

8. 2006: Hector Scoffington-Gordale, M. A. (Oxon.) appointed HM Chief Inspector of Schools

Expectorate!

'The bastards,' they chortled,
'retiring at last!'
With laughter their faces glowed red.
'Well, I'd hope,' Mac parried,
extending their mirth,
'the buggers don't tarry
upon the fair earth
but, promptly discerning
the little they're worth,
get summarily stuffed and drop dead!'

Blackley Park Road, looking from Blackley Library to Blackley Institute,
Tudor Avenue and Lewis Rec (the David Lewis Recreation Ground), 1968

10

To *Mailbag*, the *Hebers & Tonge Telegraph*

Sir,

Ref: Court injustice

In the case of the three poll tax debtors gaoled by Middleton magistrates unanswered questions abound.

Releasing them almost immediately, Mrs Justice Ebsworth of the High Court described their sentences as 'horrendous'. So I wonder whether the *Hebers & Tonge Telegraph* is now in a position to shed some light on the subject because, in this regard, other newspapers serving the community have signally failed.

Certainly, this newspaper has already made a significant contribution to the debate by highlighting three aspects relating to the involvement of Rochdale Borough Council's Treasurer's Department. First of all, we have been told that it is the Treasurer's job to collect monies owed to the Council; secondly, that a prison sentence necessarily rules out any chance whatsoever that monies due may be collected by the Treasurer; and, thirdly, that the Rochdale Borough Treasurer 'does not want anyone to go to prison', despite an earlier report to the contrary.

All these things very much needed to be spelled out, but other questions remain. For instance, how did this absurd situation arise in the first place. As I understand it as a layman, magistrates, being amateurs like myself, rely on the magistrates' clerk for professional advice about the law. So what went wrong in Middleton?

Did Middleton magistrates fail to seek the clerk's advice? Did the magistrates' clerk fail to give the right advice – or fail to ensure that Middleton magistrates properly understood the advice that was offered?

None of this is unimportant because this issue goes beyond the rights and wrongs of the poll tax. What we should perhaps be more concerned about here is the freedom of the individual and the duty of the courts properly to interpret legislation enacted by parliament.

Who are the magistrates who orchestrated this farce? Why are they the only ones who have been allowed to hide under a cloak of anonymity?* Or are we to take it that the Middleton bench is at fault in its entirety? And, in either case, what steps are being taken to safeguard against a similar situation arising in the future?

And, finally, why has it been left to the Labour group to complain to the Duchy of Lancaster? This is a Civil Liberties issue, so where are the LibDems? It's also an issue about Law and Order, so why haven't the Tories spoken up?

Yours,

Byron Marlfield
Mainway, Middleton.
8 July 1993

> * No explanation was given; Middleton magistrates retained
> their anonymity.

Blackley (Daughters of the Cross) Convent, corner Rochdale Road/
Parkmount Road (late Lewis Avenue), 1958

11

The Perpetrators: a Fable of Our Time

"We have noticed over the past few weeks gangs of youths wandering about bent on trouble; door bells being rung; the occasional bottle being smashed; regular screaming and shouting; rubbish being strewn in gardens. Perhaps if we kicked out the sociologists and the social do-gooders and bring back [*sic*] flogging and hard labour we might get somewhere, because that is the only thing these scum understand."
Mailbag, the *Hebers & Tonge Telegraph*, 3.10.80

It was more than he could stand, the last straw. At the precise moment that Basil Hanlith placed his cutlery in the dead centre of his dinner plate, wiped his lips clean with a table napkin, and reached for the remote control handset in order to adjust the colour on his television set, the better to appreciate Sue Lawley's complexion (or was this the Rippon girl who had done the high kicks on the Morecambe and Wise Show?), three things happened in quick succession. A milk bottle smashed in his driveway, someone screamed like the devil, and his doorbell played the introductory eight notes of 'Colonel Bogey' in the key of G.

'*Gott in Himmel!*' cried Basil, who had holidayed in Hamburg and Oberammergau since his retirement and was in the habit of essaying samples from the phrase book which had accompanied him on those outings.

He leapt to his feet and rushed out into the hall, his mind agog with bitter memories of those gangs of youths he had spied in the last few weeks wandering about bent on trouble. And even as he snatched the riding-crop from the shelf in the hallway beneath the print of the Gainsborough pastoral scene (*The Brook By The Way* – from the picture in the Vernon Gallery) he knew what he would find – rubbish dumped in his garden. Even so, he was totally unprepared for the trail of devastation that awaited him when he threw open his front door.

For strewn across the lawn and lapping like a wave the lower levels of the rockery and the bed where he cultivated Alpine

72

plants, lay – at a conservative estimate – upwards of fifty copies of the local paper. But, to compensate him for this atrocity, the perpetrator had on this occasion had insufficient time in which to effect his escape. The youth lay supine at Basil's feet.

Triumphantly then, Basil Hanlith – teacher, retired headmaster, holiday visitor to Hamburg, Oberammergau, Anzio and Monte Cassino – brought the riding-crop down hard across the shoulders of the already-snivelling youth.

'Take *that*, you young thug,' he cried, 'and *that* . . . and *that* . . . and *that* . . .'

'Mist-oh!' piped a thin voice in protest.

Basil ignored this. God knew they had ignored his own entreaties for long enough. 'Ob-viously,' he intoned, as he began to beat the youth in time to remembered strains of *Pomp and Circumstance*. (Basil had seen all the films – *The Longest Day*, *633 Squadron*, *The Great Escape*, *Sink the Bismark*, and he had served in the Ministry of Food for the duration.) 'Ob-viously . . . your pa-rents . . . don't give a damn . . . where you are of a night . . . just as long as . . . they don't have to . . . put up with you . . .'

'Mist-*oh*!'

'Nor . . . do you appear . . . to belong to . . . this neighbourhood.'

'Me *leg*, mist-oh!'

Basil paid him no heed at all, having finally discovered what his right arm was for.

'Bottle,' said the youth hoarsely – then even more so: '*Bleedin'*.'

'Perhaps if we kicked out . . . the social do-gooders . . . and brought back *flogging*!'

Basil Hanlith stopped as abruptly as he had begun. Slowly, as if he were hearing an echo of the youth's words, their meaning dawned on him at last. The lad had cut himself on the milk bottles Basil had left out for the Express dairy: he'd been ringing for assistance.

Somewhat desperately now, Basil Hanlith threw down the riding-crop and bent forward in an attempt to succour the unconscious youth. (God! What if it was an *artery*?) But helping the lad proved to be more difficult than he had anticipated, because the empty newspaper delivery bag, the front of which advertised the *Hebers & Tonge Telegraph*, kept getting in his way.

Deep inside his gut, Basil Hanlith felt the first stirrings of a sensation which had been experienced by so many Japanese prisoners of war and which had been alluded to, Basil seemed to recall, in the film version of James Clavell's *King Rat*. It was a sensation such as that which signifies the onset of an attack of dysentery or, in Basil Hanlith's case – Basil having served in the Ministry of Food for the duration – of the runs.

Mr Mac's shop, Marlfield Street, late James Street

12

Canticle

I did not like you, Edward Heath,
With rictus smile and Osmond teeth,
And shrugging shoulders underneath,
I did not like you, Edward Heath.
I did not like you Harold Wilson,
Gannex- éd tyke in ivory Hilton,
Weaving words like broadloom Wilton.
I did not like you, Harold Wilson.
I did not like you, Margaret Thatcher,
But judgment day will surely catch yer,
And God with pious cant will match yer.
I did not like you, Margaret Thatcher.
I did not like you, Dennis Healey,
Horrendous-browed, I adjudged you really
Of Commons' wafflers, mouthed most mealy.
I did not like you, Dennis Healey.
I did not like you, Enoch Powell,
Apoplectic from the bowel,
Feeding hatred through each vowel.
I did not like you, Enoch Powell.
I didn'y like thee David Steel,
Tha ken ah didn'y know thee wee-ll,
But all the same . . . Och, what the hee-ll!
I didn'y like thee, David Steel.
I did not like you grumbling Jim,
Stern of feature, weak of chin –
Whose diatribes would foul my bin.
I did not like you grumbling Jim.
I did not like you Tony Blair,
With Batman-Joker smile and hair –
I truly think you didn't care.
I did not like you Tony Blair.

Who else? Oh, save your sympathy
For all poor souls who just like me
Must watch dissemblers on TV,
Our endless craven company,
Blow and spout and puff – and *be*
The nadir of fraternity.
For when such folk I'm forced to see,
Then most of all, I don't like me.

Dwellings, Rochdale Road, opposite the Farmyard Hotel, 1968

13

To *Vox Pop*, the *Gruinard*

Sir,

When we were on holiday on the Costa del Sol earlier this year my twelve year old son spotted an advertisement hoarding bearing the images of the three Euro candidates for the region and this prompted him to sum up the Euro elections thus:

'I get the picture, dad,' he said. 'You vote for Specky or Baldy or Beardy!'

Our own Beardy failed to contact this address prior to the recent Euro election, though our Baldy and Specky did. So it was a toss up between them – quite literally.

Because neither one of these Euro clones was known to me by name; nor could their political records or intentions be deciphered from the cheap bumph that was shoved through my letter box. Yet each of these candidates was asking me to vote him into a job that would pay him £31,678 per annum, plus £155 a day subsistence allowance, plus £2,131 a month for office expenses, plus £70,000 a year for secretarial assistance.

Still, I suppose someone's got to win the jackpot.

And I strongly suspect that our Euro candidates deliberately cultivate their personal anonymity in much the same way as lesser mortals who hope to come into a fortune stick an X on their pools coupon, requesting no publicity.

Yours,

Chrys McClintock,
Rhodes Village, Middleton.
16 June 1994

14

For Avis

Hi Avis

Hope your all keeping well & looking forward to Christmas. Just to let you know if you don't already. I'm still with Ray who I met last year he's very special to me. I love him dearly in my own way but its not the same love as I still have for Richard (OR HAD) I've done things & been places I've never ever been to & done before. I've been to Ireland twice/Scotland a few weeks ago as well as other places in England but the best of all are the holidays in the Med – Cyprus, Tunisia, Greece, Bulgaria, Tennerif. its been a good year for me. rearlly. I can't let a man like that go can I? I genually know he loves me but I'm getting there. I hope someday I can love him the same. Richard's been a terrible fool. he's not at all happy he's always bin thrown out (he's still a drunk.) it seems' she throws him out when he's got no money. he's even bean known to sleep in a child's wendy house & a Shed. what a life, what a fool still he's got a child by this girl now so she still & always will have a hold on him. if not her then the GSA. I don't know if its supposed to be hush! hush but I've heard his brother Roger's (Queenie's Roger) buying a house. & Richard's supposed to be moving in to it (by himself) so he's not a very happy bunny is he. Silly Silly man. Whats it all about Avis? I wish I could get hold of him give him a good shake. & tell him what a bloody fool he's been. (Parding my Frensh.) but I think he already knows that. he's lost his son & our Sheila never hardly hears from him these days he'll phone her occationaly (?) says he's going to see her & never turns up. he'll go to the pub instead and tell her (his girlfriend) that he's been to Sheila's surtely she must smell the Stale Cider on him, I could, she knows surely he lies to her she told Sheila once he's always lying to her, she said I know now why your mam threw him out. I didn't throw him out HE LEFT ME so he lied about that. he's life must be lies, & more lies all the time. do you know the baby isn't down on the birth certificate as his (it's down as father unknown) it's so she can claim more benefets thats how much love she has for him to let his son not to have an official surname. it's only Casio when it suits her. What a life hey! Anyway Avis love to yo All. And Mery Xmas when it cums.

Melanie X X

Harpurhey
Manchester.

12 August 1976

Mount Carmel School, corner Shepherd Street/Rochdale Road, 1958

15

Perm Any Two From Three

If I should die think only this of me . . .

. . . Yeah, just like you always done.

Fat Chance

There's more of you for me to love
Before Weightwatchers gives you a shove
To halt the spread of fatty tissue –
So ere you shrink, just lemme kissue.

Harpurhey Flea Market from Trisian's Café, 1999

It's time to go down to the Flea again,
to the Land of the Pre-Softened Shoe,
Where someone has worn the string vest I'll try on
and the verminous underpants too;
Where Camp coffee's best black,
Frank Yerby's still read –
and fifty Barnes Greeners*
Have kipped in the bed;
where CDs may be warped,
Stax singles all scratched –
And a slaphead sells garments
Versace can't match;
Where hair may be orange,
the air itself blue –
That keyboard I covet
quite tacky with glue.
For, there – from yon vendor
with Nike shod feet! –
Tis time to select
one's thrice-threadbare suite.

* Barnes Green: a sub-district of north Manchester

16

To *Prie-Dieu*, the *Catholic Self-Servist*

Madam,

Two things fascinate me about correspondents to your newspaper at present.

First of all, some of them appear to imagine that the Catholic faith in this country has been borne thus far from pre-Reformation times by a succession of indigenous noblemen, heedless of any contribution from six generations of Hibernians.

And secondly, whilst half the world is starving, far too many of them are pre-occupied with their own sexual proclivities – particularly where these happen to coincide with what novelist Anthony Burgess describes as an "inversion", the free practice of which has given rise to a disease which threatens to kill the half of the world that is not starving.

Yours,

The Very Reverend Canon Fr Thomas Pavor MA, STL, RD *
St Joseph of Cupertino's Presbytery
Blackley, Manchester.

18 September 1996

* Written by Eddie Ealingham of Blackley whom experience has shown that an assumed provenance represents his only guarantee of publication

17

Another Rock and Roll Christmas

Pitiful it was. Yeah, that's the word I'm looking for – pitiful. I
mean, the way she was going on with herself, there. See, first off
she give this horrible high pitched scream, like as if she'd fell
down a lift shaft. Well, sort of halfway between a scream and a
shout, it was really. A shriek, I suppose you'd call it. Went right
through you, it did. Set your nerves on edge. Enough to set
anyone's nerves on edge, you ask me. Because you could feel
everyone sort of jump in their seats, like as if to say:
   'What the *hell's* up with her, for Chrissake?'
   Not that anyone said that, of course. They looked it though –
sort of wide-eyed, looking round at her, heads twisting right round
to look at her if they had to. And glancing from one to the other –
tut-tutting too, a few of the old dears. And one feller across the
way from where I was sat went: 'Jeesh!' to no one in particular,
and spilt some coffee on his hand from this polystyrene cup he
was holding at the time. Yeah, there was fifty of us in there that
afternoon – well, not far short of it anyway. Forty maybe. Thirty-
five, forty, summat like that, there was – and every last one of us
is now looking round at this fat tart going on with herself, like as if
to say:
   'What the *hell's*. . .'
   Well, yeah, I've already told you that, haven't I?
   Oh, and then she starts sobbing like she's never gonna stop.
Real heart-rending sobs, they was, like as if her little baby has
upped and snuffed it on the spot.
   Chance'd be a fine thing! I thought. *No such luck with her
little baby!*
   Still, every cloud has a silver lining, they say, and at least
with its fat mother going on with herself like that – screaming or
shrieking, or whatever you wanna call it, and sobbing her heart out
too . . . Yeah, at least with its fat mother going on with herself like
that, her little baby, that's a toddler, really – has stopped skriking
at long last, and has turned its two minute attention span to tipping

the entire contents of its fat mother's handbag out on the waiting-room floor for want of summat better to do while its fat mother is blocking the doorway through to the drinks machine so no one can get in or out if they fancy a cuppa – and is going on with herself like them Ay-rabs on the *News at Ten* when the Ayatollah snuffed it that time.

For God's sake, Miss Piggy, shut your fat yap!

Not that it worried me, mind – this fat tart blocking the doorway to the drinks machine like that. Because I'd already had a cuppa coffee about five minutes ago, and it was manky. So no way did I want another one. Slung the first one down the bog, most of it. Fifty pee, it cost us too! Fifty pee down the drain, thank you very much, Crumpsall A&E.

Mind you, I suppose manky coffee from the hospital drinks machine was all I had a right to expect really, being just part and parcel of the sort of day it had been from the start. Up at the crack of noon to cash me Giro, dodging the drizzle while I done a bit of a guttering job for Avis' mum. (We still got on okay, the old girl and me, after me and Avis split up. Besides I could always trust her to give us cash in hand the Social never known about.) But what with us rushing the job a bit because I'd got better things to do, the day it was, and with the heavens opening all of a sudden around about half past two – well, I'd only went and fell, awkward-like, from halfway up next door's ladders I was using and gone belly-up on to Avis' mum's coal shed roof. Agh! – it felt like me ribs had gone. Yeah, a right sod of a day it had been from the start – and now this!

'Oh, whatever's the matter, Mrs Malhamdale?' says this tart from the hospital, coming through from where the doctor is with her clipboard and her pen, and hearing this fat tart going on with herself like this. Hospital uniform, but not a nurse. No, summat else. God knows what, but official – like an *almonder* maybe. 'Oh, whatever's the matter?' says Marc Almond's mum from the hospital.

So this has her off even worser, this fat tart, Fatty Malhamdale. Now someone's showing her a bit of sympathy at last. Dead ringer for one of them fat Dutch tarts in that Dutch

84

feller's painting, she is. (Pieter Bagel or summat. I dunno.) You know, the one where there's loads of people sat at these tables, shovelling food down their fat necks at a Christmas party or summat – and there's some other blokes out in the snow. Or maybe it's another painting, that. I dunno. But it's very seasonal – I do know that. Not that Fatty Malhamdale's shovelling food down her fat neck, though she has obviously had plenny of past experience of that sort of thing. But at this precise moment in time Fatty Malhamdale is just stood in Crumpsall A&E, sobbing her fat heart out.

Jeesh! Give it a rest, can't yer?

I mean, she's really on a roll with this sobbing malarkey – hey, and spitting out words too, though words that make no sense, like a foreign language almost:

'Ah-SOB-ony-SOB-lefiffer-SOB-fireminny-SOB-fireminny-addermoce-SOB-an-SOB-somebdee-SOB-nicktit!'

Double Dutch, the lot of it! Looks like a fat Dutch tart, *sounds* like a fat Dutch tart. Because Mrs Almond from the hospital don't seem to be any the wiser, hearing Fatty Malhamdale going on with herself like this. And neither does anyone else from the looks of things.

So Mrs Almond from the hospital puts her clipboard and her pen down on this trolley full of bed pans and spittoon-things at the back of where I was sat, and says for Fatty Malhamdale to: 'Come and sit down a minute, Mrs Malhamdale and I'll fetch you a nice cup of tea.'

Hey, no favouritism, please, Mrs Almond! Get her a manky cup of coffee like I just had.

And she looks round then, Mrs Almond from the hospital to see where Fatty Malhamdale's stuff is, and seen where the toddler has tipped its fat mother's handbag out on the floor – lipstick, lip salve, Saver Seven card, house keys, family allowance book, Avon & Test Supa 8 Debit Card statement, Atrixo hand cream, Kleenex tissues, Wilkinson's kiddy wipes, collapsible brolly, bobble hat – and is now playing with this Tampax in a wrapper like it's Winston Churchill's cigar or summat and he's looking for someone to give him a light.

'What's she *on* about?' I said to this feller sat opposite us with his right arm in a sling and his left one shoved in the sleeve of an anorak that looks like he's used it to wipe the bog floor. 'Moanin' Minnie, there. What's she on about?'

'Search me,' says Bog Wipe, and farts.

Oh, I'd rather not, if you don't mind, pal. Least, not till I've had me hippy tight arse jab!

Still, Mrs Almond's got Fatty Malhamdale sat down by now. And this other bint from the hospital, the younger one that's been coming through every two hundred years or so and calling people in to see the doctor in this hoity-toity voice she has – bit of a fancy-pants, she is (you know the type) – this younger bint that's made up to buggery and has a bit of a weight problem like Mariah Carey (Mariah *Scary*, more like). Well, Mariah Scary's bent right over showing everyone next week's red, white and blue washing while she helps Fatty Malhamdale shove her stuff back in her bag while Mrs Almond trots off to fetch her a nice cup of tea.

Fly the flag for England, luv, that's the way!

'With or without,' trills Mrs Almond, turning to ask Fatty Malhamdale before she pushes though the door to the drinks machine.

'Without, please,' says Mariah Scary, spokesperson for Fatty Malhamdale as the toddler shoves his fat mother's Tampax up his nose and screams the house down

Without the tea, Mrs Almond, if it's as bad as the manky coffee!

'She's lost her purse, she has,' says this old cow with an hearing aid in both lugholes and a striped tea cosy on her head, who's sat next to Bog Wipe – who rips another one off.

Oh, a deaf interpreter of Double Dutch wi' no sense of smell. That's jus' what we need!

Because how Mrs Teapot's sussed this one out, I'll never know. But she has, you know. Yeah. Because this Irish slag three chairs down from us – bandage round her head, face like a bag of spanners, chirps up then:

'*Nicked*, sure 'twas. Get-na' norange juice for the bairn, an' leaves it atop o' the press for a minim.'

86

Well, begorrah! thinks Oi. *An' bedad!*

'She'll have been a bit mithered maybe,' says Mrs Teapot, 'wi' the kiddy skrikin' an' that.'

Mithered? Be out of me kin tree, had a kiddy skriked like that.

Oh, and they was all at it then, twenny to the dozen. All forty of 'em. Well, thirty, twenny-five maybe. Because while this has been going on, there's one or two been shown in to see the doctor by Mariah Scary. Correction: twenny-nine maybe. Because Mariah Scary calls out again then in this hoity-toity voice she has:

'*Drusilla Aardvark-Stampede!*' And this anorexic Zombie in Doc Martens and a duffel-coat folds her *Living* magazine in two and creaks across to the consulting room, legs moving stiff as a clockwork soldier.

Hup-two-three-four, hup-two-three-four!

But the twenny-nine that's left behind in the waiting-room is at it hammer and tongs still. Well, twenny-eight, I suppose. Because I'm not involved in their stoopid conversation. 'Purse . . . nicked, nicked her purse . . . happened to our Grizelda on the MIP Market on her birthday . . . had her purse nicked, she did . . . Ooh, our Betty's Rumpelstiltskin had his wallet lifted in ASDA's when he was tryin' on one of George's string vests . . . Conran Street Market, a week last Tuesday, they only made off with our Godzilla's Constellation suitcase full o' duty-free cigs . . . Always the same this time o' year . . . Seen a feller do a runner with a lettuce, Church Street, Newton Heath, last year . . .'

'How d'yer know?' I asked Mrs Bag O'Spanners.

'Sure, an' how do I know whath?' says she.

'She's had her purse nicked.'

'Now, isn't she just after sayin' so?'

'*God res' you, murray gennul-men . . .*' sung Perry Como on the telly.

Cheers, Perry! Yeah, thanks for that!

'Never heard nowt, me,' I said. 'I mean, apart from her goin' on with herself, there.'

'She's upset. Wouldn't you be?' pipes up this skenning bag, Cruella de Dog Rough, sat next to the telly, squinting up with one eye at the TV screen, and down at a copy of *Chat* with t'other.

Oh, tell me, pretty maiden, are there any more at home like you?

'Upset?' I said. '*Upset?* Well, I suppose I might be if I had a purse, for one thing. An' if I was daft enough to leave it lyin' around with money in it, for another.'

'Who said anythin' about money?' says Cruella *Sherlock* de Dog Rough, as Mrs Almond come back with a cuppa manky tea for Fatty Malhamdale that looks exactly like a cuppa manky coffee. But at least it shuts Fatty Malhamdale's yap for her while she takes a few sips of it.

Drink deep, and die, Miss Arbuckle!

'What yer tranner say?' I said to Cruella de Dog Rough.

'I'm not tranner say nothin',' says she. 'All I'm sayin' is no one's mentioned money but you.'

'So?'

'Well, who's to know there's money in her purse? 'Cept her and the one 'at nicked it?'

'If there's no money in her purse,' I said, 'then why's she cryin', clever-hole?'

She says nowt then, Cruella de Dog Rough: just looks at us, gormless-like.

'Well?' I said. 'She cryin' because her *empty* purse is a valour-ble fambly heirloom in tooled leather or summat? Or because she's got money in it?'

'All I know is someone's nicked her purse, that's all.'

'Strikes me you don't know much about nothin' then.'

Oh, and then *he* only has to go and stick his oar in – Mr Bog Wipe, opposite. 'You was in there,' he says.

'What?'

'You,' says Bog Wipe, a gilbert dangling from his nose. 'You was in there, gerrin' yourself a drink after she went in.'

'So?' I said. 'The world and his kin *wife* was in there this afternoon at one time or another.'

'*Language, please!*' says Mrs Almond, rounding on the pair of us like Denis Norden with her clipboard and her pen in her hand.

It'll Be Alright on the Night, will it, darlin'? Somehow I don't think so.

'You gonna get the cops or what?' says Bog Wipe, turning round to her, green gilbert a-dangle.

'Yeah,' I said. 'Fetch the coppers. I'm gerrin' accused of summat I never done, here.'

'*Malcolm-ah David-ah Wildebeest Rut,*' says Mariah Scary, all hoity-toity from the doctor's doorway. And up I get – *ouch!* slowly – because it's my turn at long last.

Hey, and a fat lot of good it done us too. Because Dr Iqbal Bananarama, or summat, reckons me ribs is just bruised, not broke – and, even if they was broke they don't strap ribs up at Crumpsall no more. But here's a prescription to get some painkillers from the dispensary. So that's it – twelve hours at Crumpsall A&E – and all I've got to show for me trouble is a prescription and a cheery goodbye. Kin NHS! Good mind to take me custom elsewhere in future – like the Alliance on Rochdale Road maybe, or the Millstone down in the dip, or the North Parade up on the Avenue East, where two pints of chemick costs a good deal less than an NHS prescription does nowadays.

'You right, dad?'

'Right as I'll ever be,' I said. 'Where's your motor?'

'Round the front on Delaunays.'

But Spike's scarcely got the words out of his mouth before there's another hullabaloo – this time outside the door to the gents' bog where Bog Wipe, fresh from wiping duty no doubt, emerges waving one purse, empty, Fatty Malhamdale's, for the use of.

'Get the police!' he says.

Bleedin' Norah!

Plus Fatty's off again then: *Flight of the Valkyries* this time round, chunnering on in Dutch like before – or maybe German, it was now.

'Ah-SOB-ah-SOB-fiffy-SOB-quiddinair-SOB-byme-SOB-chissma-SOB-owfy-SOB!'

'Gimme me coat,' I said, getting hold of it for meself from the back of the chair where I'd left it, shoving me – *ow!* – right arm through the sleeve with difficulty. Then – *ouch!* – the left, at which point I nearly fell flat on me back because the toddler is only toddling under me feet now, tranner shove its fat mother's

Tampax in me shoe – and I sort of trod on him more or less. So now he's off skriking again.

Oh, for Chrissake!

'Come here, come on, come on, there you go.' Spike's in on the act now. Always very good with kiddies, Spike. Tube of Smarties, they'll follow him anywhere. And as Spike picks the bab up, Bog Wipe says again:

'Get the police!'

At which point Mrs Almond from the hospital reaches for the telephone receiver, and Malcolm David Wild (that is, yours truly), what first addressed a captive audience on his wedding day way back in the Year Dot, and who has since been prevailed upon from time to time to act as MC at family parties and the like (not to mention a good few shindigs at the North Parade before his ex-wife Avis got took on as a barmaid there), said Malcolm David Wild gets up on his hind legs and takes to the floor in the waiting-room of A&E at North Manchester General Hospital.

Before he utters a word Mr Wild is seen to grab a bed pan, or a spittoon perchance (whatever it is is metallic), then he bangs it three times, gavel-like, on top of the trolley till silence prevails.

'A gavel an' a giggle!' If pressed, thus might Mr Wild describe his public speaking technique: 'One to grab their attention, t'other to hold it.'

Security in the shape of a half-caste lad, Selim, guarding the exit door, moves in on Mr Wild at this juncture. But Mrs Almond, replacing the telephone receiver, deters with that same hand and a timely glance Selim's intended closer acquaintance with Mr Wild's coat collar as he commences his address to the assembled company:

'Christmas comes but once a year,'
An' when it does, I want a beer.'

The required giggle materialises as intended, courtesy of a scattering of folk whose literary exploits never progressed beyond the rhyming couplets in the *Rupert* Annual.

'The trouble is I'm not gonna get no beer if the coppers get involved. You neither, none of yous. Christmas Eve, it may well be, but if I know the coppers, we'll be stuck here in A&E till midnight. 'Zat what we want? I wouldn't think so for one minute. We've all got better things to do tonight, haven't we?

'Now, this young lady, Mrs Malhamdale – what's your name, luv? Your first name . . .Wyn? . . . Wynona, eh? . . . Well, Wynona here's had her purse nicked, as you very well know. An' someone here done it, they say. There again, for all we know, the one 'at done it is someone who was in this waitin'-room earlier this afto but is not in this waitin'-room no more. And at this very moment, ladies an' gentlemen, while we're stuck in A&E till midnight once the coppers come, that same person is laughin' up his sleeve at us. Because he's already spendin' what he pinched off Wynona in the tap room of the Cleveland Hotel maybe, or the Millstone down in the dip. Or for all we know, he may be miles away by now – in the Grove, say, or the Charlestown, up near the Fourways, or the Old David's, Alkrington. An' meanwhile, Billy Muggins – that's you and me, both – yeah, Billy Muggins is stuck here in A&E till midnight once the coppers come. Plus Wynona here's still got an hole in her purse, plus she's still gotta sort out the little un over Christmas . . .'

'*Mairead Macquarie-Shark Attack!*' says Mariah Scary from the doctor's'doorway, and Mrs Bag O'Spanners makes as if to rise from her seat.

'Now, if you'll gimme one minute of your time, ladies an' gents,' says Malcolm David Wild, his voice awash with good cheer. 'One minute of your time is all I ask – and a smidgeon of your charity too on behalf of Wynona and the little un in this festive season . . . Whasser kiddy's name, luv? . . . Orlando, eh? Well, with your permission, lays 'n' gennulmen, on behalf of Wynona Malhamdale and little Orlando . . .'

Mr Wild takes from his coat pocket a flat cap, which he unfolds – and from the back pocket of his denims he pulls a small bundle of notes from which he extricates a five pound note bearing a portrait of his sovereign lady, the Queen, plus (on the obverse side) a study of her namesake, the penal reformer, Mrs Fry. Then, depositing said fiver in his unfurled flat cap with a gesture of profligate abandon, he passes the cap onwards via the good offices of Mrs Macquarie-Shark Attack, who is awaiting Mariah Scary's further instructions with regard to an appointment she has with the good doctor under her given name, Mairead Maureen McCorquodale.

'How much they pinch, Wynona? . . . Any idea? Twenny? Thirty? . . . *What?* Fifty-*five quid?* . . . *Fifty . . . five . . . quid?*' Mr Wild's anger is almost palpable at this stage in the proceedings. 'Now, you heard her, ladies an' gentlemen? Wynona here's short fifty-five pounds sterlin', an' she's got the little un to fend for over Christmas. Lays 'n' gennulmen, you may please your good selves, of course. But I'm in for a fiver, whatever it may please you so to do. So how's about it, lays 'n' gents? An' I would respectfully suggest to you that you look into your hearts before you look into your purses or your pockets, as the case may be. An' if you've only got coppers to spare, well, think on . . .'

At this juncture Mr Wild takes – *ouch!* – little Orlando up into his arms and, averting his nostrils as best he can from the odour of ammonia and worse drifting vertically and insistently towards them, he jiggles the child in his embrace, making him chuckle:

'Christmas is comin', Wynona's been let down flat,
So please put a quid or two in my flat cap.
If you haven't got a quid, a fifty will do,
If you haven't got a fifty, well – PARP *– to you!'*

The toddler enjoys the lip-fart best of all. He toddles off, chuckling still, when – *ouch!* – Mr Wild places him before the assembled company together with his conclusions in the matter:

'Because when it comes to Wynona Malhamdale, here, who's got little Orlando to take care of in this season of goodwill, I would respectfully suggest to you, lays 'n' gens, that every penny counts! I thank you. An' God bless!'

Mr Wild's cap was duly passed around the room at his behest, and none can say that the hospital staff was not to the fore when it came to contributing thereto. True, there were some amongst the outpatients who simply had insufficient wherewithal from which they might reasonably have been expected to contribute. And certainly the cap, having done the rounds, contained some fifty pence pieces in addition to pound coins, plus a sprinkling of smaller denominations of silver. Consequently – Mrs Almond having been elected to cash up prior to making the presentation to Wynona Malhamdale in recompense for her earlier loss – consequently, the grand total is found to amount to £50.37 in all: exactly £4.63 short of the projected target.

Upon hearing this from Mrs Almond's lips Mr Wild will not hear of a recount – nor will he countenance a further appeal to all and sundry. Instead – and from that same back pocket, from the contents of which he initiated the impromptu collection – Mr Wild now extricates a tenner, and tossing it atop the cash total lying before Mrs Almond amongst the bed pans and spittoons, he asks only that she allocate to him a fiver in change. Accordingly, Mrs Almond sets before him five pound coins along with his cap – and, as she does so, there bursts from the two dozen people present in Crumpsall A&E at twenty-nine minutes to five on this Christmas Eve afternoon a spontaneous ripple of applause which so embarrasses Mr Wild that he turns on his heel without another word and, scooping up the five pound coins, makes – with cap in hand and son Spike in close attendance – for the exit without once looking back.

Had he paused to do so, Mr Wild might have been further embarrassed to note that Mrs Teapot (as she is known to him) and Mairead Maureen McCorquodale (as she is not) are not the only ladies with tears in their eyes – and that the outpatient known to him simply as Bog Wipe (Mr Raphael S. Heathbank, as his medical record reveals him to be – a ten pee contributor to the collection) is heard to utter a vulgar two word expression inviting anyone within earshot to initiate coition upon his person. Whereupon, Mrs Almond, who is definitely within earshot, and is even more definitely disinclined to accede to his suggestion, responds with a swift two word rebuttal of her own, as heartfelt as it is instantaneous: '*Language, please!*'

'Bobby Driscoll,' I said. 'I was jealous of him once upon a time.'
    Eh?'
    'Bobby Driscoll in *Treasure Island* – him on the Avon & Test advert on the telly. Clever, innit?'
    'You mean?' said Spike.

'The way they rig it like that. Put the words in their mouths, him an' Robert Newton.'

'Robert Newton?'

'Long John Silver – in that advert for the Avon & Test Supa 8 Debit Card.' I done this Punch an' Judy sort of a voice then: '"Pieces of eight, pieces of eight! Get ya pieces of eight with an A&T Supa 8!"'

'It's the parrot says that.'

'Cap'n Flint.'

'It's the *parrot*.'

''S what I said.'

'No, you din't.'

'Cap'n Flint *is* the parrot, berk!'

'Oh.'

'It goes "Pieces of eight, pieces of eight" an' that – an' Bobby Driscoll, who's Jim Hawkins, the cabin boy, turns to Long John Silver, who winks at the camera, and says . . .'

'Wot a load of bollocks!'

'Be a laugh if he did. More truthful, if you like. But it's clever, innit? You reckon she was maybe took in by that?'

'Who?'

'Carol Vorderman.'

'Carol *Vorderman?*'

'No, stoopid! The fat tart at the hospital.'

'Wynona?'

'Yeah.'

'What about her?'

'Reckon she was maybe took in wi' Squire Trelawney, Dr Livesey an' the rest o' the gentlemen eggin' her on to get herself an Avon & Test Supa 8 Debit Card that she can run up a bill with that's eight times her ann'al income, an' have nowt left, come Christmas, 'cept what's in her purse? Or, rather, what *isn't* in her purse, as the case may be.'

'What d'you care?'

'I don't.'

'Well, what you goin' on about then?'

'*Another Rock an' Roll Christmas*!' sung Gary Glitter on the juke box in the lounge at the North Parade for the umpteenth time that afternoon.

'Oh, it's summat I was thinkin' about when I tried usin' the hole in the wall at ASDA's jus' now.'

'Funny thing to think about . . . Same again?'

'Nah. I've gotta get back.'

'You in tonight?'

'North Parade? Nah. Your mam's on, i'n't she? Berkshire maybe. Jus' for an hour or so. I'm knackered, the day it's been. 'Sides, sooner you get to bed, they say, sooner Santa comes callin'.'

'It's all right for you. I've gotta put a bloody pool table together yet; shove a brace of triple-A batteries up My Little Pony's backside, knowin' my luck. What've you asked him for this year then?'

'Oh, you know.This 'n' that. Nothin' fancy.'

Like me Christmas Giro, for a start . . . and twenny quid cash-in-hand for the guttering job I done for Avis' mum . . . and an Avon & Test Supa 8 Debit Card that's no good to man nor beast without Wynona Malhamdale's PIN number . . . and forty-five quid, courtesy of that same lady's purse. Well, thirty-five, as it's turned out, due to me having to subsidise her *fifty-five kin quid* that she never had in her purse in the first place – the lyin' little minx! Well, no – not *little*. No, I can't in all honesty say that. But Wynona Malhamdale is certainly no fatter than Mariah Scary, if truth be told. Nicer too when she's not crying. I'm sure I seen her in the Berkshire one night last week, now I come to think on. Reckon we'd make a good team, me and her – Wynona Malhamdale and me. Plus her Avon & Test Supa 8 Debit Card from out of her purse, of course, that I can work the arse off it till the cows come home once I get her PIN number off of her. Better still, there's no toddlers allowed in the Berkshire after half past eight at night, skriking or not, Christmas Eve or no! Which has gotta be a definite bonus, it seems to me.

'Right, drink up, Spike,' I tells him. 'I'm due in the Berkshire at half past eight. Ah,' I says, stretching. 'It's a grand life, as long as you don't weaken. Still, God rest you merry's what I say!'

'You're pretty chipper, considerin' your bruised ribs an' that. You on a promise or what?
'Well, you never know, do yer? Bein' Christmas an' that.'

Harpurhey Baths, corner Shepherd Street/Rochdale Road, 1958

18

To *You Don't Say*, the *Daily Mess*:
[EXTRACT] the Unpublished Letters of Chrys McClintock

. . . and I must take Jacqui Everglade to task with regard to her
stated objection to "septuagenarians like comic Douggie
Carlingford squiring children". (*Downtown,* 5 May) S*quiring*, she
tells us! So is Ms Everglade perhaps accusing Douggie
Carlingford of child abuse? If so, I think she should come right out
and say so. Because to the best of my knowledge, the only crime
of which Douggie Carlingford is guilty – if crime it be in Ms
Everglade's book – is that of *siring* a child in his seventies . . .

'ITALIAN HOSTAGE EXECUTED' screams your headline
article (by Our Own Correspondent, Jamie Messerschmidt, 15
March), which goes on to detail the most recent cold blooded
murder in Iraq . . . Language like this, being highly emotive, is
regrettable in the extreme. For it may tend to militate against the
peace process whilst lending a spurious legitimacy to the
perpetrators of the atrocity. Because "Execute", v.t., according to
my *Oxbridge Concise Dictionary* at home, means "to put to death
according to due process of law", this being the very last thing
terrorists should be allowed to lay claim to . . .

. . . and so I put it to you that Andrew Gutter's editorial comment
(13 Feb) regarding footballist Cy Ickornshaw's recent racist aside
errs on the side of unthinking racism. Because, when Andrew
Gutter seeks to mitigate Ickornshaw's offence on the grounds that
"he was speaking in private to a friend", he was never more wrong
in his life. This is to miss the point entirely. For the fact of the
matter is that nobody in his right mind even *thinks* that way any
more . . .

. . . to say I found your recent headline report (by Our Social
Affairs Correspondent, Tex Crowshoot, 9 September) about a
"gang" of 63 failed asylum seekers who "terrorised the streets of

Manchester" worryingly emotive. Quite possibly "these people have no valid claim to reside here", as the Home Office avers. But it is a different thing entirely to adjudge them "perpetrators of shoplifting and criminal damage rife within the inner city" simply because the powers-that-be *believe* them to be responsible. I can only hope that these 63 human beings who have been "thrown out of the UK" may find a safer haven in a country where guilt must be established by legal process rather than by GMP/Home Office diktat . . .

. . . so it was interesting indeed, though hardly illuminating to see Ex-Teacher, Chorlton (*You Don't Say*, 2 December) coming out in favour of VAT on children's clothing. During three decades spent in schools in and around Manchester I came across not a few teachers of this sort. They had never been kids themselves, and had no conception of what family life is like on a day to day basis . . .

The New Inn, corner Moston Lane/Rochdale Road, 1968
(Site of the new North City Library and College)

19

Fiducial Times: *Rewind & Revue:*

I LOVE THIS, YES I DO

Dee-Jay U E Jay revisits the Embassy Club
with *The Very Best of The Merseybeats*

The Very Best of The Merseybeats is the very best CD in my collection. Not that I'm much of a CD collector, as you very well know – more of superannuated, dyed-in-the-wool, fusty-dusty vinyl freak. Hey, and a 45 rpm vinyl singles freak while we're about it too. Reason being, there are far too many one-hit wonders I'm crazy about for me to be worrying about accumulating an album collection. I mean to say, why on earth would I need or require the *20 Golden Greats of Zager and Evans* by the one-hitters of that name? Be tantamount to setting my cap at a unicorn's nest, methinks. And what pop-picker in his right mind would want to include *John Fred and his Playboy Band's Greatest Hits* on his Christmas gift list? (John *Who*? I hear you say.) Nope, gimme 45 rpm, 7-inch vinyl singles anytime – I love 'em! Though that doesn't mean I don't love this Merseybeats' CD too.

Talk about money well spent! What an absolute ring-aling-dinging humdinger of a collection this is! With the sole (soul?!) exception of 'Sorrow', a truly regrettable omission, let it be said. Okay, so 'Sorrow' was released by The Merseys – and it's big band-tainted too, if we're gonna be pedantic about it. But with this one exception (hurriedly rectified, I might add, via my 10,000-strong singles collection), *The Very Best of The Merseybeats* is the definitive Merseybeats' collection on stilts!

Yep, all their hits are here, every last one of them as far as I can see. It ain't nothing but a 20 track cornucopia of a Merseybeats' singles *fest* with knobs on, of which my personal high notes are the classic 'Mr Moonlight' – originally the B-side to 'I Think of You' (some B-side!) and a rendition infinitely superior to The Beatles' offering on the *Beatles For Sale* album;

also the unfairly underrated 'I Stand Accused'; and 'Last Night I Made a Little Girl Cry'. (This last title, though it postdates The Beatles' 'She Loves You' by a full twelve months, I always like to think of as its prequel.)

With a repertoire outstripping that of The Animals (well, go on, then – name me any four Animals' singles without looking them up in the *Guinness Book of British Hit Singles*) and, quite possibly, The Byrds – The Merseybeats lacked (luckily for me, a fan of long-standing) the compositional skills of The Beatles and their continuity of line-up. (Billy Kinsley and Johnny Gustafson came and went almost at will, it seems to me; Aaron Williams gave up altogether from the mid-Sixties on – and, barring 'Really Mystified' and 'See Me Back', I can't truthfully say I'm overly keen on any track carrying a Tony Crane/Johnny Gustafson credit.)

On the other hand, it is these perceived professional shortcomings that I, personally, hold dear. Because this is precisely what keeps The Merseybeats (and myself by affiliation) ever Sixties-based and (in my mind's eye – okay: a pig's!) eternally young.

Yes, for me, The Merseybeats will ever retain that quintessential tang and twang that so distinguished the guitar-based beat music of the early to mid- Sixties. And consequently, whenever I hear Tony Crane's distinctively nasal tones backed by Billy Kinsley's and/or Johnny Gustafson's quasi-percussive guitars, I am back once more – a time traveller no less! – in Bernard Manning's World Famous Embassy Club (*circa* 1965), where The Merseybeats look and sound just as they always did. Hey, and *moi aussi*, if ya don't mind, pal. Full head of hair, girl(s) on my arm, pint of Tetley's bitter and a Player's Medium cigarette on the go, 21 years-of-age and nobbut 9 stone 10 pounds in an Italian-cut three-piece suit, white shirt with separate collar and knitted tie with a dinky knot, Timpson's winklepickers and a Crombie overcoat from Burton's on Piccadilly – boozed up on (hic') another Saturday night. (Well, as boozed-up as three or four pints of Tetley's Mild will get you!)

Happy days, eh?

Hey, you just bet ya sweet ring-aling-dinging life, they were.

Correction: happy days they are *still* – at least they are back home in *fin de siècle* Playa de Las Americas, Tenerife, whenever ya very own DJ U E Jay feeds the *Very Best of the Merseybeats* CD into the Bar Barbarossa house system just as often as the clientele will allow.

Junction of Rochdale Road/Moston Lane, 1959
- the New Inn to the left

20

Three Quakers

Once upon a time at the youth club he had asked Lorna Humesett to dance and she had refused. Buddy Holly was singing at the time, and the song Buddy was singing was 'Maybe Baby'. The next song Colin Leitrim, the MC, played was 'Tell Me How', the flip side of 'Maybe Baby'. The kids had only brought half a dozen or so records to the youth club that night, so 'Maybe Baby' was played four or five times between eight o' clock and ten o' clock when the youth club chucked out. The same went for 'Tell Me How'. Neither one of them was the best track Buddy Holly had released to date.

He thought the best Buddy Holly song of all was 'I'm Gonna Love You Too', the flip side of 'Listen To Me'. He liked 'Listen To Me' too, but it wasn't a dancing record. Not that 'I'm Gonna Love You Too' was a dancing record really – not unless you did a slow jive to it, like you had to do with 'It'll Be Me', the flip side of 'Whole Lotta Shaking Going On' by Jerry Lee Lewis. Not that It would be him now. He certainly wasn't Gonna love her too, seeing how Lorna Humesett hadn't Listened to him when he'd asked her to dance, so there was no Maybe, baby, about it. No, he wouldn't have wanted her to Tell him how any more. Hey, and there wasn't that much Shaking going on that night in any case, not with only half a dozen records to choose from, there wasn't. Anyway, he was a Quaker, not a Shaker. So, that was it: fin-*ee*; the end of the good times they might have had, he and Lorna Humesett. You wouldn't catch him asking Lorna Humesett again. Hey, no way. You wouldn't catch our boy asking any girl more than once: he was a Quaker in that respect, like his mother, though his mother was a Quaker in a different way.

'I'm a Quaker,' his mother would tell him when he was small and he had maybe refused a second helping of treacle pudding or an ice cream cornet when Pandolfo rang his bell in the street or when the other kids were going to the matinee at the Empire cinema on a Saturday afternoon and she'd asked him if he wanted to go. 'Come on, it's make your mind up time,' his mother would say. 'I'm a Quaker: I'll only ask you the once and no more.'

The Society of Friends, the Quakers, would thereby be ridiculed through no fault of their own, and by means of a manner of speaking that was almost creakingly quaint in that it was just another of those inherited clichés that were as much a part of their shared family life as the photograph album with the dusty red cover in the pages of which he knew that, on opening it, he would always find a photograph of himself singing 'Dearie' on stage at the children's concert at Queen's Park Hippodrome on Turkey Lane when he was eight years of age, or where his grandfather, aged 21, would always be smartly turned out in a First World War uniform bearing the insignia of the Lancashire Fusiliers; his father in that of the King's Own during World War II; and his Grandma, in her sixties, standing, smiling, outside Mrs Thurrock's house on Glen Avenue on Coronation Day, 1953. Thus, in the privacy of private parlance at their house on Cockcroft Street, where you were a Quaker because you would offer a favour just the once, you were invariably too, if noticeably restless, said to be 'in and out like a dog at a fair' (an occasional, inexact alternative being 'in and out like a yo-yo' – 'up and down' being said to be effected like 'I don't know what'). Also, it was generally agreed to be like 'Muldoon's picnic' or 'Fred Karno's circus' whenever a gathering was well-attended and casually organized.

But as far as our boy could make out, asking somebody just the once and nevermore had no connection whatsoever with Quakerdom. In his mother's case it was a reference to being what she would alternatively call 'a careful Christian', by which she meant somebody who was loath to part with a penny piece, and who – though proclaiming to the world a staunch adherence to the Christian ethic – would, if they offered charity at all, offer it just the once, lest repetition of the offer might induce acceptance of whatever it was that had been so reluctantly offered in the first place.

Anyway this was what his mother meant when she said she was a Quaker, whether or not this was the way real life Quakers were – and, in all likelihood, they probably were not since no

Quaker was known to the family except for the fat chap sporting a smug smile and a tricorn hat on the Puffed Wheat carton and the porridge oats they sometimes had in the winter with Tate and Lyle's Golden Syrup mixed in.

No doubt something of the Quaker ethic had been lost in the translation via the word of mouth Chinese messages of successive generations of the family, just as something had indeed been lost in the translation of his mother's limited understanding of the Quaker ethic to the governance of his own conduct. For if our boy were to have said he was a Quaker when he offered something (which is something he never did, in fact, say – just thought) he would have meant exactly what he said, and nothing more. There would have been no inherent reluctance behind the gesture, no underlying fear of acceptance; no, none whatsoever. There would simply have been the certainty, ultimate and absolute, that if our boy were to offer something or ask for anything and have that offer refused or request turned down, then never ever in this mortal coil would he offer it or ask for it again.

Which is exactly the way it was with Lorna Humesett. One night at the youth club (he couldn't have put a date on it: 1958/59 – somewhere in around there) he had asked Lorna Humesett to dance, and Lorna (for whatever reason) had refused; and another boy had taken her home. Ergo, never would Lorna Humesett be asked again. Not by him she wouldn't. Hey, no way! Though this is not the same as saying that Lorna Humesett would not change her mind about him.

And Lorna Humesett *did* change her mind about him, as he had known she would do all along. The only thing he did not understand was how he had always known with an almost cast iron certainty – even as far back in time as the Friday night at the youth club when they had not danced to the Buddy Holly song – that this is exactly what would happen: Lorna Humesett would change her mind about him. Oh, yes; and when Lorna Humesett changed her mind about him then nothing would do for her other than that she would have him.

Maybe the songwriter Percy French had it right about the female of the species: 'if you want them for an after, sure, you look the other way', though in the case of our boy, of course, he no longer wanted Lorna Humesett. Being a Quaker – well, being our boy's kind of Quaker – he had never so much as looked in Lorna Humesett's direction again subsequent to that night at the youth club when Buddy Holly had sung, undanced to by the pair of them. And thereby, of course, he positively guaranteed what most attracted Lorna Humesett to him from round about the time Cliff Richard was singing 'Living Doll' and every pop star in the world was called Bobby or Billy or Tony or Ricky or Vince, and the only thing 7-inch vinyl pop singles were short of was a bit of pink ribbon tied round them in a bow, though this would obviously have made them unplayable— which would, of course, have suited him and his mates right down to the ground because they got the 'Summertime Blues' pretty bad over all that schmaltzy stuff for four seasons of four years from February, 1959, till the Beatles came along to give pop music a bit of welly once more.

'You must be kin barmy,' said his best pal at Christmas, 1961, when he'd told him he wasn't interested in Lorna Humesett – nope, not in any shape or form, he wasn't. 'Some kin shape,' said his best pal, laughing at him. 'Some kin form. Never hit it off with the girl, personally. She's prob'ly short-sighted, prob'ly. Went out with that mate of hers once, Francine. Kin goer, her, that Francine . . .'

'Who?'

'Frisky Francine – her whose dad does the fish on the market.'

'Oh, her.'

'Babysittin' one night. Kinnell! Had 'em off before they was out of the street . . . No, not the baby's, berk – hers! Ha, ha, ha, ha, ha. She was only a fishmonger's daughter but she lay on the slab an' said fillet! Ha, ha, ha, ha, ha. Geddit? Tell you, I was glad when they come back early from the Embassy Club with a chip supper from that chippy next foor to Aplin's. Kin knackered I was . . . Hey, but that Lorna – now she's somethin' else.'

'Eddie Cochran,' he said.

'Eh?'

105

'Eddie Cochran number: 'Somethin' Else' . . . *Dah-dah-dah-dad-dad-dad-dad-dad-dad-dad-dad-dad-dad-dad-dad*!' The air guitar needed a touch more presence.

'Oh, *that*.'

'Length of hosepipe down his pants.'

'What?'

'Time we seen him on at the Odeon on Oxford Street. He had this length of . . .'

'They call it a Dido, that,' said his best pal, who'd been around, but only around their way. 'Tart in north Africa invented 'em, summat BC. Hey, but change the subject, why don't-cha? What about Lorna Humesett? You gonna give her one or what?'

'I don't like her,' he said.

'Par-ding?' said his best pal. 'Do I hear you aright? You don't *like* her? What's that gotta do with it, may I ask?'

'I just don't *like* her.'

'Why? What's not to like? You barmy or what?'

And 'or what' was, of course, the answer to his best pal's question. Because he was a Quaker, which was reason enough for him, though he chose not to share the thought with his best pal. Still, maybe his best pal was right about Lorna. She was certainly a bit of all right to look at things clinically; and neither had she been backward in pushing herself forward whenever he was around.

One time at the parish dance at Middleton Baths where they used to lay wood flooring down over the plunge and have the Bum Notes up on stage (as he and his mates called the five cadavers – Les Langfield and the Lounge Lizards – who would attack the roofspace with muzak from braying brass instruments, a snare drum and a piano) . . . one time at Middleton Baths when he was seventeen and the cadaver at the keyboard was playing Floyd Cramer's 'On the Rebound' in waltz time, Lorna Humesett got Bazzo to try and set up a foursome: Bazzo with Elsie Kimberley, our boy with Lorna Humesett – Bazzo going off with El, taking it as read; he, like a smacked arse (he'd had a few, it should be said), leaving Lorna Humesett stuck in the middle of the dance floor all on her todd, and going off to volunteer the solitary single lyric of

'Tequila' on stage when the Bum Notes essayed it in ragtime, prior to rooting a couple of Black Velvets and Molly Casio out of the bar area and taking her home at the end of the night.

Or a couple of months later, when he'd got the invite to Lorna Humesett's party at New Year in the same street as the Jackson's Febrifuge factory – what was it called now? Across the road from the Cintra Cinema, later Gala Bingo Hall . . . Brewster Street? And he'd only ended up (with upwards of thirty people in the house that night) all alone with Lorna in the upstairs front bedroom (God alone knew how she'd rigged that one), and he had done no more than ask her where his coat was.

Elvis Presley had been singing 'His Latest Flame' on the red and cream Dansette record player in Lorna's living room when he had gone back downstairs, and gone off home with Marie Tute, telling her she was the Marie in the song.

Liar!

Then, came that other Christmas Eve, the next Christmas Eve, at Pamela Wembury's house, when things really did get a bit out of hand. This was one Quaker who had had a fair bit to drink that night, and had kept it down for a change – a half dozen gaseous pale ales and as many vodkas chasers too, whereupon Lorna Humesett had plonked herself down in his lap, said lap becoming, on his rising from his seated position, his thighs that lifted his legs up the thirteen Axminster-carpeted stairs leading to Pamela Wembury's bedroom before Elvis Presley had sung 'Return To Sender' (the Christmas number one of that year) for the seventh time that night. And in Pamela Wembury's bedroom, on Pamela Wembury's bed, athwart eighteen assorted topcoats and Rhoda Rishworth's golf umbrella that Malcolm David Wild, aka Idle, and Bernadette Holwick had beaten bodily into a welcoming concave shape earlier on in the evening, he had given Lorna Humesett what his best pal would have described as 'one', and 'one' which (had his best pal been a shade more articulate) he might have also described as 'roistering' – indeed, 'rollicking'. Then he had taken Lorna Humesett home and left her there, never to return. It would be Christmastime once more before he would see her again.

He had gone down to Conran Street Market to see about some

ex-juke box singles that this chap used to sell on the market at a stall facing the rear entrance leading on to the croft – 'Walk On By' by Leroy Van Dyke in particular, which he'd missed when it charted earlier in the year and now had a yen for. But instead of vinyl singles he picked up a twelve inch LP, *This Is Fats Domino* with 'What's the Reason I'm Not Pleasing You' on the playlist (new millennium worth, £60, according to the *Record Collector Rare Record Price Guide*, though you would never get top whack for stuff like that, maybe half that, if it was mint, and this copy certainly was not mint, though it played well). And, turning away from the record stall as the Beatles were singing 'From Me To You' on 45 his eyes met Lorna Humesett's eyes, then dropped to another pair of eyes (smaller, yet brighter) that belonged to a child of two, three months – certainly no more than that – unmistakably a girl, that Lorna had pushed before him in a Silver Cross pram.

He double checked those eyes: they were his own eyes; no, they were Lorna's eyes . . . No, again: they were his eyes *and* Lorna's eyes.

'Lorna,' he said in a low voice, and swallowed. 'Do we need to talk?'

'Oh, I don't think so,' said Lorna Humesett brightly. Already she was turning away from him. 'No, that's the last thing on earth we need to do.'

Lorna Humesett, it dawned on him – and not without a sense of regret now it was too late for them – Lorna Humesett had become a Quaker in much the same way as he himself was a Quaker. Maybe things like that were contagious. But, if that were the case, then who had he been with? Because he who had been a Quaker, he had become . . . he had become nothing. No, he had become something worse than that – he had become something sub-human.

He stood where Lorna Humesett had left him and watched her push the pram through the crowd and into the market hall that once upon a time had housed the Princess cinema. Then, turning, he left the market via the gateway to the croft, and as he went he spoke one word to himself sharply under his breath:

'*Untermenschen!*'

Mr Irlam had taught him this word in the top class at St Joey's. It had been a form of abuse in Hitler's Germany, Mr Irlam had said. It was an extremely useful word, Mr Irlam had said too. For it might be relied upon as an unfailing character reference for anyone who would take it upon himself to utter it. Rarely, if ever, said Mr Irlam, did it properly describe the object of the intended abuse.

Mrs Wykes' record shop, corner of Acton Street/Moston Lane, 1968

21

Voyeur

I seen this girl I'd marry tomorrow
If I could have me say –
With green-grey eyes,
A complexion sallow
An' hair she does – which way?

Yeah, I seen this girl I'd marry tomorrow
'cept there's nowt that I can do.
'cause it's ages since
I married and mellowed,
An' got me children too.

But I seen this girl I'd marry tomorrow
If only she'd allow.
Just to have that girl
I'd beg, steal or borrow . . .
'er husband? Oh, he ain't nowt!

Hey, I seen this girl I'd marry tomorrow:
Their house is on our street –
An' I'd even take
Them three little horrors,
The kid's what's round her feet.

Boy! I seen this girl I'd marry tomorrow,
Me eyes was stuck like glue
One night her lights
Went on bright yellow –
An' I seen her in the nood!

Oh, I seen this girl I'd marry tomorrow:
A fortune I would bid.
So it's just as well
I had the sense
To marry her when I did.

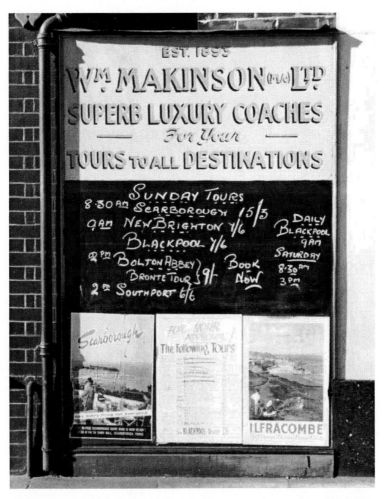

Sign, Makinson's Coaches, opposite the New Inn, Moston Lane, 1959

22

Five Card Stud

Byron Marlfield compares his concern for the Third World with a game of five card stud. First of all, says Byron, you become concerned about the Third World; then you personally do something about it; thirdly, you continue to be concerned; fourthly, you get your MP to do something about it; and, finally, you get your friends concerned and get them to do something about it.

By the time he was twenty-one years old in 1965 Byron Marlfield had already taken on the responsibility of caring for Amanda (the Loveable – the Clubable of later years). But one night in the July of that year, whilst he was availing himself of the teatime mixed grill he set so much store by, Byron Marlfield happened to catch sight of some of his Mozambiquan brethren on the early evening news. No mixed grills had they – a mixed grill would have probably killed them. But there was no probability attached to Byron's next observation: they were most definitely being killed by starvation, a lack of good drinking water, and an overabundance of strutting soldiery armed with the AK-47. Byron Marlfield had played his first card in this game of five card stud: he had become concerned. Soon he played his second card: he covenanted himself, and, by the time of the Live Aid concert in 1985, he had played cards three, four, and five. Byron Marlfield continued to be concerned, and so were some of his friends by this time. Heck! Wonders would never cease – there was even an MP or two at it by this time.

MARLFIELD ESTATES

To Gazumper, *The Obverser*

Sir,

Your correspondent's suggestion (*Baksheesh*, 18 September) that investors and companies might lend financial assistance to the developing countries is not as far-fetched as it might at first appear.

Under Resolution 2626 of 1970, the UK is pledged to give to the countries of the Third World 0.7% of its GDP. Yet, twenty-four years on, the present government coughs up less than half this amount and, as was recently demonstrated by the Pergau Dam affair, misdirects even this.

However, there may be a way in which the Government might be forced to honour its commitment.

If every person who pays income tax were to covenant 0.7% of his gross income to one or other of the Third World charities, the extent of the Government's contribution would be decided for it – and in a manner that it would have to weigh very carefully indeed in electoral terms if it were then tempted to move the financial goalposts with regard to covenants.

Yours,

Byron Marlfield
Prestbury, Cheshire
25 September, 1994

23

The Killing

When I seen she was there again I was that mad I put the boot in hard as I could and she went smack against the wall and fell, awkward-like, and lay there all crumpled in the corner of the room. I was gonna kick her again but she was just sort of lay there and I couldn't kick her like that, not like that I couldn't. I was still mad though.

I suppose that explains it. Because I don't know what got into us then, but I turned her over and undone this cloth belt-thing on her frock and I pulled it out through the little loops and I propped her up against the wall and got the belt round her neck and tied it in a knot that I pulled that tight you couldn't never get it undone even if you wanted to; and I picked her up's what I done then and lifted her and hung her on this chrome hook that's screwed to the bedroom door, right up at the top. Then I sat on the bed and looked at her hung there on the back of the door.

'Stoopid bitch!' I said, as if she could hear us. 'Bloody stoopid bitch!'

But when me breath begun to come more easy and the redness cleared from behind me eyes I seen it different. She had her hair tied in these little pigtail things that come down from under this sort of a cap she was wearing and her eyes was shut like she was only asleep, and in the light from the window her whole body seemed a sort of a purpley-blue that matched the forget-me-nots pattern on her frock.

It was then I realised what I'd done. So I lifted her down quick and tried to get the knot undone then, but me hands was dead sweaty and I'd tied the knot that tight I known I wasn't never gonna get it to shift, no matter how hard I tried.

'Come on . . . come *on!*' I went, like she could hear us or summat.

But she just lay there like the stoopid rag doll that she was. Close up too she smelt of fresh apples like Shirlee always done, and I seen her lips was parted just a teeny bit, like an egg shape, only red – like she was screaming fit to bust.

'Come *on*!' I said again, and I must have shouted it or something, because next thing I known I could hear Shirlee's voice at the foot of the stairs.

'What's going on up there?'

And when I never answered her:

'Tony . . . what're you doing up there?'

Oh, I shouted back then all right, because I known it was no use and I'd never get the knot untied without cutting it, so Shirlee was bound to find out. 'Miss-friggin'-Muffet's what I'm doin',' I shouted. 'People 'at don't look after things when they're bought 'em but leave 'em lyin' around the bedroom floor all day long shouldn't never be bought nothin'. Never mind flippin' nightdress-cases!'

I could hear Shirlee coming up the stairs then, and I known there'd be trouble.

Blanchard's drapery (formerly Estall's grocery), corner of Walter Street / Rochdale Road, 1968

24

Tealeaves

It's easy to dismiss Dismas*
As a common or garden thief,
Though they say he relented –
And even repented
At a rate that defies belief.

It's simple to fix upon Nixon
As the all-time inveterate rogue.
Yet, those snide perorations
Hide our own perforations –
Hypocrisy was ever in vogue.

It's witty to skit at the British
As an errant piratical band:
Tight-fisted four-flushers
Who pinched Typhoo bushes,
Depriving gross rajahs of land.

It's silly to castigate Adam –
So silence those jeers and that boo!
When he nicked that fell truffle
Crowds joined in the scuffle
With this cry: 'Is it one lump, or two?'

* Dismas, the Good Thief, one of two thieves crucified alongside
Christ, the other being Gestas.

25

To *Mailbag*, the *Hebers & Tonge Telegraph*

Sir,

The landlord of the Gardeners Arms, Middleton Junction, whose charity pop concert was curtailed following complaints from neighbours may be interested to learn that he is not the only one who has had a visit from the police this summer.

Nine o'clock of a summer's evening on the occasion of my home-based Silver Wedding celebratory bash brought the forces of law and order to my own front door with a complaint from an anonymous well-wisher.

The cause of the offence? Loud music, perhaps? A Bacchanalian booze-up on the back lawn? A frenzied orgy that had spilled out on to the Queen's Highway to frighten the horses and inconvenience the number 59 bus?

Nothing of the sort. It seems the kids were making too much noise on the bouncy castle.

In retrospect it occurs to me to wonder when kids last made too much noise on a bouncy castle in Sarajevo.

Yours,

Chrys McClintock
Rhodes Village, Middleton.
10 September 1992

26

Between Earth and Sky

'You'll be leaving us then?' George Latchly asked rather than said as they reached the grass verge of the play area where the benches had been positioned.

They had crossed the shopping precinct in slanting October sunlight and they sat where, given half a chance and clement weather, they always sat, on the little wooden bench under the tree.

'What makes you say that, George?' said Derek, teasing the older man.

George Latchly pushed his peaked cap to the back of his head and stared. 'Well, either you said summat about handing your notice in, or I imagined it,' he said bluntly.

'Aye, so I did,' said Derek.

That morning he had spent a good ten minutes behind a closed door in the postmaster's office and as soon as he returned to his section and began sorting the mail for the second delivery, George had quizzed him. But Derek, not wanting Old Lippy to catch him 'wasting good government time' now he desperately needed a favour from him, had fobbed George off with a promise to explain over lunch.

He said: 'You know Estelle's been mitherin' to move back to the Manchester. Well, when you were off yesterday afternoon, I went and handed my notice in.'

'Sugar me!' said George, removing his cap altogether and scratching the top of his head. 'An' there's me thinkin' you'd settled in right well an' all.'

Basking in the balm of George's bewilderment, Derek unwrapped the aluminium foil containing his lunch. And before a crumb of it had passed his lips, he sensed Estelle had packed his favourite: slabs of cheese, topped with peppered slices of tomato. For some reason the taste of cheese and raw tomato always made him think of picnics in the country. In the cheese he would rediscover more than a hint of the summer sun, as if he breathed again the warmth of fields waist-deep in golden corn and the tang of heather and gorse, gusting from hazy Pennine peaks. Then, just as he imagined himself a weary traveller, dry-throated with an unquenchable thirst, his teeth would release the red tide of tomato juice to slake the dry channels of his tongue. And for one second Derek felt his heart swell with a terrible pride, as if the surging arterial blood within might burst its banks on a floodtide of sheer satisfaction. For to Derek Keld at that moment the simple fact that Estelle had gone to the trouble of preparing his favourite sandwiches (oh, all right: *butties*, as she teased him for calling them) was, like a kiss remembered, a tacit but unmistakable reminder of her love for him. And he found this doubly reassuring, because in recent weeks he had begun to have his doubts.

From where he and George were sitting they could see the new precinct full of shoppers in their bright winter coats. It was market day, and though it wasn't much of a market, there was a sufficient variety of stalls to bring a bit of excitement to the workaday image of the little town – a cheap biscuit man, a cheap greetings-card man, a cheap meat man, a cheap greengrocer, a cheap bread man – cheap, but not nasty, the cheapness being arrived at by means of shrewd marketing practice in purchase and sales. Near sell-by date stock, quick and extensive turnover (something which Byron Marlfield at MOnrOvia TV, where Derek had worked on leaving school, referred to as 'piecemeal wholesale', by which Byron meant that you effectively got rid of all your stock in one fell swoop, even though it might take you a day or two to do so). Yes, it was cheap all right, but not nasty. Anything nasty got left. And that was the very best lesson in merchandising, Byron said – if you were left with stock on your hands. Because when you put your money where your mouth is and you come unstuck, you learn very quickly indeed – either how to do the job properly, or to leave well alone.

Since moving here two years ago, Derek had tried whenever possible to eat his lunch in this exact same spot. Geographically speaking, it was the centre of the town, though Derek preferred to think of it as the heart. Sitting here, eating his lunch, he felt as if he were part of it all; as if he were being allowed to see things take

119

shape and grow, to witness the final flowering of the original blueprint. When they were first married, and whilst Estelle was still working at the telephone exchange, he had met her here each day at noon. But, for the past twelve months, it was George Latchly who had been keeping him company.

A broad, square-flagged – well, piazza, he supposed you could call it, where Derek could remember there being only clinker underfoot, gave safe pedestrian access to a colony of shop units that glistened like pueblo dwellings in the sun. One day a squad of council workmen had driven up in a tipper truck. They dumped a thousand old stone setts on the plot where the Avon & Test Building Society now stood, and during the week that followed, Derek had watched as, laughing and blaspheming, they laid the setts amongst the flagstones, arranging them in geometric patterns, cementing them to the ground.

From the parks department came stocky men, beetle-browed with wind-slapped cheeks. They hefted spades and augers and planted birch trees between the setts. From time to time they revisited the site and he would see them in amongst the trees, tending bulbs and bedding plants according to the season. A little further across, beyond the play area where toddlers screamed the slide in terrified delight, stood the welfare clinic, the white expanse of its walls punctuated at ground level with trolleys and perambulators, and – higher up, above the rectangular entrance way – with a solitary aerosol-sprayed word *SKY*: two-foot high and bright vermilion.

Derek broke off a piece of crust and tossed it on the ground, whereupon a starling dropped down from the silver birch that stood above them and, eyeing the two men with suspicion, proceeded to goad the bread with its beak. Derek brushed bread crumbs from his lap, smoothed the aluminium foil wrapper.

'She's not settled then, the missis?' said George.

'Not really. She's been a bit homesick for a while now.'

George Latchly stroked his chin thoughtfully, riffling his bristles like shale. 'Ah, well, maybe it does take some gettin' used to. It's an overcoat colder when it wants to be too. Missin' her family, is she?'

'That's the main thing, I think.'

George smiled. 'I had similar trouble with my missis – what? – five year since. We stuck it out though. "Lucy," I told her, "you've got to give the place a fair trial." Which she did do, as it happens. Which is what *you* want to do, Dek: give it a fair trial. It'll be all right, you'll see.'

'Oh, it's all right you talking,' said Derek, 'But it's easier said than done. I mean, it was okay at first, when we were both out at work all day. The trouble began when the little un arrived. Estelle's the first one with a baby on our estate, and with the neighbours being out at work during the day, many's the time she won't see a living soul till I get home of a night. Says she feels like a prisoner. Driving her barmy, it is.'

'Rowin', are you?'

Derek nodded, his mind shying away from last week's memory of broken bottle glass riding Duerr's mixed fruit jam to the kitchen floor down a wall he had decorated with an expensive Vymura on his last few days off work. 'You can say that again.'

'You've gotta pull together where there's kiddies involved,' said George.

'I know all that,' said Derek. 'But you can take just so much and no more. You can't keep comin' home to rows night after night. Anyway, like I say, I went in to see Old Lippy yesterday afternoon and handed me notice in. Reckoned I'd be better off where I come from.'

Oh, that did it! That did it all right! Yeah, that had Latchly off, it did!

George told Derek he could remember comin' back to Manchester after the War and wonderin' what the hell he'd been riskin' his life for. He'd celebrated his twenty-first birthday in a wadi outside El Alamein (he had) when all there was on the menu was bully beef – desert chicken (he said they called it). And George could remember thinkin' at the time (he said) that none of the hardship and the discomfort . . . sand in your underpants, scorpions in the bog, gerbils in the bread ration – hey, and they were welcome to it too. Stale, at least a week old, hard as iron, like a ship's biscuit (it was), break your teeth on it (you could), better off without it (you were), more nutrition in a sweaty sock (there was), if they'd had any socks in the first place (that is) – if they'd even had the feet to put the socks on (some of them). Why, he could remember a lance-jack who . . . And what had he (George Latchly) come back to after the War? The same old Manchester (he said): dirty chimleys, bomb sites, cobbled streets still, trams like rust buckets, airport for the nobs, Cromwell cockin' a snook at the workin' man across from Exchange Station, no new buildings but council property (Labour council guaranteein' a Labour vote), burglars breakin' into council houses (hell's bells!), River Irk (fumes from which) would have poisoned Jabez Clegg (*The Manchester Man*) before his cradle got as far as Red Bank – hey, and runnin' into a dirtier river still (the Irk, into the Irwell), black as an alderman's heart (it was), stunk like an old horseblanket (at best) and a carboy of mixed chemick (at worst), said George Latchly: Mancunian by birth, mill town newcomer by persuasion.

Derek folded his lunch wrapper and pushed it inside his jacket pocket. Getting to his feet, he raised his arms and stretched luxuriously. And as he pivoted from the hip in this attitude of crucifixion, he raised his eyes momentarily and noticed the leaves of the silver birch that rose above them had turned a crisp golden-brown, as if disgorging the sunlight stored during the summer months.

'So, when are you fixin' to leave us?' said George.

'I'm not,' said Derek.

'You're *not*? I thought you said you seen Old Lippy?'

'That was then, this is now,' said Derek, breaking into a grin. 'When I got home from work last night Estelle tells us her sister's gettin' wed in the New Year an' he wants us to look out for a house for 'em. So, I went straight back in to see Old Lippy this morning and told him to cancel me notice.'

'You twat!' said George Latchly to Derek Keld. 'You was havin' me on.'

A whoop of childish laughter wafted towards them from the play area, and they glanced across to where two swings were etching arcs between earth and sky.

'Well, go on, George,' said Derek, hilariously. 'Tell us again how you and Errol Flynn led the Allied Advance.'

'Bollocks to Errol Flynn!' said George Latchly. 'I had Neville Brand wi' me, most decorated serviceman in World War Two after Audie Murphy. You watch *The Untouchables*, Dek? Robert Stack an' that? Neville Brand was Al Capone . . . No, that was Frank Nitti, that. No, Al Capone . . . Yeah, that was my oppo, Neville Brand. Wouldn't have made it through without Big Nev. You should've seen us, pal. We come runnin' up there on to Luneburg Heath, me and Big Nev, and there's Monty givin' Admiral Doughnut, Doenitz, a good sherrackin', he was, and he turns round and seen us, me and Big Nev, and he says to us, Monty, this is: "What kept yer?" says he. Bloomin' cheek! I mean, we've only yomped it all the way from Anzio. Yeah, "What kept yer?" says Monty. So Big Nev has to smarten him up, like. So he done no more than leans across and whispers in Monty's lughole, and Monty looks a bit puzzled for a second or two, like he can't take it all in. "Ordie?" he says. "*Ordie?*" Then he turns round and says to us, to me, that is. "*Ordie?*" says Monty "You're supposed to be *dead*, Wingate! Crikey, wait till Winnie finds out! He'll have a flippin' . . ."'

Loofe's mens outfitters, junction of Conran Street/Rochdale Road, 1968

27

That's Nowt

There was me and our kid and me dad and me grandad
all sat in our parlour, watchin' telly,
when the telly blown up.

I said to our kid:
I done me Bronze Medal at Harpurhey Baths today –
you had to jump off these ladders into sixy.'

'That's nowt,' said our kid.
'When I done me Tin
you had to jump off the balcony into the shallow end.'

That's nowt,' said me dad.
'When I done me Mild Steel
you had you had to jump off the rafters into a fire-bucket.'

That's nowt,' said me grandad.
'When I done me Scrap Metal
you had to jump off the roof into a wet sponge.'

Then me grandad pulled this old brown photograph
out of his waistcoat pocket
and shown it us with tears in his eyes.

And when your great-grandad done his Stone,' he said.
'When your great-grandad done his Stone,
You had to jump off the boiler-house chimley
into a bead of sweat . . .
which is why he's not here to tell the tale for hisself.'

'Why's that, grandad?' I said.
'Break his back, did he?'
'Nah!' said me grandad, like I was thick.
Them Stones was that heavy
it dragged him right down to the bottom and he drownded –
and him nobbut a lad in short pants
that had a wife and ten kids to support.'

That's nowt,' said me dad.

Williams Deacon's Bank, corner Queen's Road/Rochdale Road, 1968

28

To Mr Vincent Irlam

Dear Vinny,

There wasn't really time enough or opportunity to speak to you last Thursday, I'm afraid, but I want you to know we are truly sorry, Annie and myself, and would like to take this opportunity of offering you our most sincere condolences at this sad time.

We've met lots of nice people on holiday over the years, but none nicer, and we can honestly say with hand on heart that you and Carmelita are the only ones we ever wanted to meet up with again once we got back home. Only circumstance prevented this, believe me, and it will ever remain a cause of considerable regret to us that we never got around to arranging the re-union we had hoped for.

We often mention the two of you and the holiday we had in Minorca back in '73. If I remember correctly, we had plenty to complain about at the time with regard to our accommodation (mildewed kitchen utensils, damp bedsheets needing to be dried in the mid-day sun etc. etc.), but we had plenty to laugh about too.

Who, I wonder, could recall without laughter having to throw open the door of a holiday chalet lest fumes from the gas stove and the smell of toast burning on the skillet should asphyxiate them? And on a happier note too, we love to tell the story of how we foraged for victuals and chanced upon that little butcher's shop in the esplanade that enabled us to live like kings for a fortnight. ('Oh, for pity's sake, Annie, NOT the fillet steak AGAIN!')

I have a very personal memory of you too, Vinny, and it concerns the time the fiesta was on and we found ourselves in Cuitadela on the Thursday before Easter when we ended up in a church that was more like a basilica. (Was it a cathedral? I'm sure I can't remember.) Anyway, the place was all decked out with flowers and decorations on a scale that certainly Annie and myself have never seen the like of before or since, with the religious tableaux that had processed through the town displayed in the alcoves, and the whole place abuzz with the conversation of townspeople and tourists alike.

As I remember it, Vinny, you and Carmelita had entered the church a little in front of Annie and myself, and glancing across to that place upon which the solitary sanctuary lamp shed its light, you walked directly towards it with Carmelita on your arm and an expression on your face as if to say, 'Ah! [*BLURRING, POSSIBLE WATER DAMAGE*]

Words cannot say how much I respect you for this, Vinny. Nor am I able properly to express my firm belief that an acknowledgment such as this, being freely given in your time of plenty, will surely be reciprocated in your present need.

God bless you, Vinny. *¡Hasta la vista, amigo!*
Sincerely,

Josephus Bunratty
New Moston, Manchester
9 September 1974

St Oswald's Church, corner Eggington Street/Rochdale Road, 1958

29

Earth

That night – the night the baby, the youngest one, had its first convulsion – well, when he got to bed afterwards and tried to get off to sleep, things just kept going round in his head like the big wheel at the fairground – turning and turning ever so slowly, and it seemed at first as if it was never going to stop.

He just lay there and he kept thinking to himself it was going to stop any minute now and he'd be able to reach right into it and get his little kid out of there and then he'd be able to get his head down because everything would be all right at long last. Except that it didn't stop. The big wheel just kept right on turning and his little kid was always at the far side of it or right up at the very top of it where he couldn't reach in and grab him and bring him out of it safe and sound. Yes, he just lay there while that was happening; and maybe he was dreaming, and it was horrible, because all he could do was to lie there helpless in the dark, seeing nothing (except when he closed his eyes and saw the big wheel), and listening intently for the baby's breathing in the cot next to the bed. Because Estelle was asleep now, Estelle having the ability to switch off like that. Yes, Estelle was fast asleep. He could feel her next to him, warm as toast, her breathing steady and smooth, and the baby was asleep too, though the sound of the baby's breathing was quieter and a lot shallower than Estelle's breathing.

There was a lorry – a two-tonner, it was, at least from the sound of it – and the lorry was climbing the hill towards Summit and taking ages about doing so, and something kept tapping at the bedroom window every now and then, like this – tick! – so he couldn't be sure if he'd heard it or not, and it made him listen all the more intently. Then – oh, it must have been about half past two at least by then – it started to rain. Really chucking it down, it was, and if he listened in a funny kind of a way it didn't sound like rain at all, but as if the whole world was on fire, and only in their little house on the Summit Estate was everything quiet and breathing and still. Except for Derek Keld, that is, who was tossing and turning and unable to get his head down properly because of the big wheel, and knowing he'd be knackered for work tomorrow (which was already *today*) because of it.

And then right out of the blue he got cramp in his left foot and it was murder and he felt like crying out, though he couldn't, of course. So, he rolled over and got out of bed and hobbled about on the Lancaster foam backed carpet in the dark. But Estelle turned over as if he'd disturbed her then, so he went out on to the landing and through to the bathroom. And as soon as he put the light on in the bathroom there was no big wheel any more, just a bog-eyed physog that Derek Keld knew only too well, looking him straight, though somewhat blearily, in the eye from the mirrored door of the bathroom cabinet above the sink.

And the Derek Keld in the mirrored door of the bathroom cabinet was a very different Derek Keld from the Derek Keld who had first moved into the house on the Summit Estate, carrying Estelle across the threshold eight years, eighty-four Post Office pay packets, three hundred and sixty-four trips to ASDA (Castleton), seven Christmases, four summer holidays, two girls, a six month old boy, three christenings, and one First Communion ago. And this very different Derek Keld was a Derek Keld that was getting a bit of a gut on him and the beginnings of a double chin too and legs like tree trunks because he was getting fed too well nowadays and was not exercising as much as he used to do because, for eight years now, he had not had to go charging about all over the place to meet Estelle after work and, for four of those years, he had been working in the sorting office all day long and not trudging the streets with a bag of Royal Mail, using up all the spare calories. And this very different Derek Keld was, in fact, the very same Derek Keld that was going to have to get himself some shirts with sixteen inch collars at Littlewoods on Saturday before his eyes popped right out of his head whenever he did his tie up.

'Imagine what you could do with all that!' Derek had said to Estelle when they'd seen Joe Horrows on the BBC Six O'clock News that night.

'Mmm,' said Estelle, with a safety-pin between her lips

because she was changing the baby's nappy in front of the fire at the time. And Estelle mumbled something else too, but Derek only heard her say: ' . . . new house.'

'Go a bit further than that, Estelle.' Derek was jealous as hell of Joe Horrows. Too right, he was, and he wasn't ashamed to admit it either. 'Hell of a lot further.'

Then around about half past six, having been at work since six o'clock that morning, and having golloped down an extra helping of one of Estelle's stew and dumpling teas with apple pie and custard to follow, and having pulled his favourite G-Plan chair a bit too close to the Radiation Hi-Speed G gas fire in the living room, Derek Keld fell asleep and snored – which fireside slumber might account, at least in part, for Derek's undue restlessness subsequent to the baby's convulsion crisis later that night. But this is how it had come about that around half past six on that February evening that Derek Keld had dreamed a strange dream as he slept in his favourite G-Plan chair in front of the Radiation Hi-Speed gas fire in the living-room of the house on the Summit Estate whilst Estelle was in the kitchen, washing up.

The strange dream that Derek Keld dreamed had voices off the BBC television news in it and the sound of the evening paper being shoved through the letter box and the sound of the baby crying and Estelle saying: 'Shu-u-sh!' to the baby, and Joe Horrows was in Derek Keld's dream too, though Joe Horrows was laughing like a madman.

In Derek Keld's strange dream Joe Horrows was driving an Aston Martin DB5 at breakneck speed down a winding country lane with loads of breathless tarts chasing after him, shouting for Joe to stop, which Joe would not do – that is, not until he glances in his rear-view mirror and sees this particular tart that he fancies, so Joe does no more than stamps on the brake pedal and jabs a secret button that works the ejector seat, which whistles last night's spent tart up out of the Aston Martin like an empty fag packet and over this hawthorn hedge at the side of the road to join all these other cows, Jersey and Friesian too, which makes room for this fresh tart off page three of this morning's *Daily Mess*, who's smiling ever so shyly at Joe Horrows with those Cinerama teeth of hers because she's having all her work cut out to keep her skirt down below her belly-button, what with the suddenness of it and with her having chased Joe hell for leather for three miles down the road in her high heels, and with her not being used to wearing clothes at all anyway, although she is a decent, convent-educated young lady really, which you can easily see, because she keeps glancing down, sort of really surprised to find herself stuck with these built-in water-wings (38 D, the caption on page 3 so described them) that are sticking out from her chest and straining the material of her white blouse that has – phew! – already popped five buttons since these items were somehow sprung on her overnight, leaving her with a school uniform that is miles too tight, poor girl – and: Hey, thinks Derek Keld in his dream, there is no way in the world you should be sulking about this, Miss Kunsthalle, Fraulein Greta Kunsthalle, all of a thousand miles from home – well, okay, pouting maybe; even though it's none of your doing, Miss Kunsthalle, Greta, so maybe you had better just come to daddy, and daddy will make things right. Yeah, daddy will make everything all right; just you see if he won't?

And when Derek Keld woke up in his favourite chair after a half hour or so and went to get the evening paper from where it was lying on the mat in the hall, Joe Horrows was there again, splashed right across the front page, where he's on some stage down in London somewhere, waving this scrap of paper about and having his ugly, laughing mug kissed by TV soap queen, Mirabelle St Henri, who plays the swell-endowed, minimally-skirted and immensely popular meter maid, Anita Beevor, on *Coruscation Avenue*, the *Coronation Street* spin-off, who has recently been maligned as St Streetwalker by *Private Ear* magazine for reasons yet to be disclosed. And the girl Mirabelle/Anita (if – age 37, as she insists she is – Mirabelle/Anita is *still* a girl) – is not dishing the dirt for once in a photogenic lifetime with Daimler-driving dieticians on St John Street, Manchester, in the opening sequence of *Coruscation Avenue* (catchphrase: 'Ooh! What I wouldn't do for an Alfa Romeo!'), but is making damned sure the camera gets the full mug shot, complete with pneumatic *décolletage* (a feature which Tavistock Greenlee of the *Sunday*

Thames once famously referred to in his piece about his stag night at the Groucho Club as 'Mlle. St Henri's undulating and blissfully bifurcated torsal panorama'). Meanwhile Mirabelle/Anita – ever the home body – is squeezing the living daylights out of Joe Horrows, gentleman, as if he's her dreamboat, come home to her at long last in her mock-Jacobean residence (*c*. 1970) in Prestbury, Cheshire, her hacienda in Mijas, Costa del Sol, or her beachside condominium on Grand Cayman.

The headline above the photograph said:

LOCAL MAN'S £253,000 WIN

'Joe Horrows,' Derek Keld called through to Estelle, though Estelle didn't hear him, being too busy with the Hotpoint washing machine and dryer in the kitchen. 'I known him when he had nowt! Nowt in his pocket, nowt in his head but sawdust, nowt in the way of mates – nowt on his backside, hardly.'

But Estelle was busy with the weekly wash now she had changed the baby and fed the kids and packed them off to their Grandpa Hanlith's for an hour or two and done the washing up. So Derek said to Estelle when he went through to the kitchen for another brew: 'Joe Horrows was the laughing stock of St Joey's, when he was in our class, Mr Irlam's, that took Standard Eight out in the prefabs, when Unzo left. Thing is, Joe Horrows wasn't in our class for a start,' said Derek Keld, reaching for the biscuit barrel and unwrapping two Gray Dunn Caramel Wafers. 'Well, he *was*, of course. Yeah, he *was* in our class. But what I mean to say is he shouldn't have been. No, Joe Horrows should have left St Joey's with Tough Titty's lot, two years before. But old Hopalong, old Hopalong mustn't have thought the world was ready to cope with the likes of Joe Horrows just yet, him being a nutter, like. So, when Joe's class left school, Joe didn't. Joe stayed put. Yeah, Old Hopalong kept putting him down a year, probably hoping Joe Horrows would end up teaming up with younger kids that were just as childish as he was.'

'Mmm,' said Estelle, getting the ironing board out of the cubby-hole so she could get at the Hoover Junior vacuum cleaner behind it.

'Just look at all those bits on the living room carpet – where *do* they come from,' said Estelle Keld, *née* Hanlith.

Of course, the only thing wrong with Derek Keld's theory about Joe Horrows' schooldays, that he continued to enlarge upon until the Hotpoint washer began its spin cycle and Derek went through into the living room to watch *Sportsnight*, the only thing wrong with Derek Keld's Joe Horrows theory of education was that by the time those younger kids arrived in Standard Eight at St Joseph of Cupertino's school they had usually grown up to Standard Eight standard in their heads as well as their bodies. Oh, there were nutters, of course, like there are nutters everywhere, but none of the kids who made it into Standard Eight at St Joey's was quite as nutty as Joe Horrows. No, those kids just kept right on growing till they reached school leaving age and never even considered what old Hopalong wanted. Joe Horrows had still been at St Joey's when Derek Keld left.

'Joe Horrows must've been nearly eighteen years of age when he left school,' said Derek Keld.

Joe Mister Fell-Off-a-Number-17-Bus-Going-Down-Valentine-Brow-Which-Is-Why-He's-a-Nutter Horrows, thought Derek Keld, as Peter Dimmock introduced *Sportsnight*. Hah! Or (if Eugene Jameson was to be believed) Joe Mister-Fell-on-His-Head-on-Cobblestones-When-He-Was-Born-When-The-Germans-Bombed-Their-House-While-His-Mam-Was-Hanging-Out-The-Washing-In-Their-Back-Yard Horrows. Well, again, hah! The very same Joe Mister Got-Locked-in-The-Empire-Cinema-Overnight Horrows, Joe Mister-Fell-in-the-Clough-Lake-With-His-Clothes-on-the-Very-Same-Day Horrows, not to mention Joe Mister Came-Crashing-Through-the-Roof-of-the-Girls'-Bogs-on-Top-of-Rhoda-Rishworth-and-Broke-Her-Wrist Horrows. Yeah, that's the boy – ha-bleeping-ha! And, latterly, just before Derek Keld left St Joey's to take up an apprenticeship at Byron Marlfield's TV shop and Joe Horrows was eighteen years old: Joe Mister Hand-Relieve-Wanker-in-the-Tennis-Pavilion-in-Lewis-Rec Horrows. Yeah, Joe Mister Total-Wanker-All-His-Flippin'-Life Horrows, hah!

Derek Keld sighed, that is, the very different Derek Keld sighed – the Derek Keld that was getting a bit of a gut on him and the beginnings of a double chin and legs like tree trunks too, and who was going to have to get himself some sixteen inch collars at Littlewoods on Saturday before his eyes popped right out of his head when he did his tie up.

But the cramp in his left foot had eased now, so he took the magazine from behind the bathroom cabinet where he has hidden it against his hour of need, turning to the centre pages where Mirabelle St Henri – 7000 days and three face-lifts younger – is bending right over the balcony of this apartment, looking out to sea on Grand Cayman, and trying (not very successfully from the looks of things) to hang out her washing on a washing line strung between her balcony and the balcony next door. Just her small things, they are, that she has somehow got dirty and can't possibly wear any more – well, not for the time being anyway. But luckily the ambient temperature on Grand Cayman does lend itself to Mirabelle being able to go around starkers, getting a lovely tan all over her because Mirabelle, poor girl, has nothing else to wear, and – what with Derek coming up on her, unexpected like he always is and probably making some sort of a noise, she's turning her head, quick-like, Mirabelle, so her yellow hair swings out to one side and her right hand goes instinctively to the staple on her bum, and she has this startled look on her face, Mirabelle, though she isn't really frightened at all, but is just surprised to see Derek, because he hasn't been expected at such an unearthly hour, though Derek is an old friend of course, a dear old friend, who is very welcome to pop in and see her anytime he wants to, seeing he is a clean-living sort of a guy who never makes too many demands of her, and besides . . . Mirabelle . . . knows that . . . sometimes . . . Derek just has to do something . . . because they can't . . . that is, Derek and Estelle can't . . . afford any more . . . little babies just yet . . . and the Pill might . . . give Estelle a coronary. . . and those other things are . . . so unnatural . . . didn't he think? . . . and a mortal sin too . . . says Estelle . . . but something . . . just has to . . . give . . . sometime . . . somewhere . . . some . . . h . . . o . . . w . . . or Derek Keld will go starkers himself, only not like Mirabelle, but in a different and more horrible way.

Derek Keld slept like a log when he returned to his bed that night.

Outside in the rain, the fires of hell were still raging, but in their little house on the Summit Estate everything was quiet and breathing and still.

The Milan Inn, corner Queen's Road/Rochdale Road, 1968

30

The *Daily Mess* (Northern Edition)

I'm a friend dropping in, not a foe falling out,
Bringing you news of an ungrateful lout.
We tipped up our cash from the day he was born
When we coughed up our rates, sent that income tax form.
We paid for his schooling, but little he learned
Save to pillage, spray slogans, vandalise, burn.
We taught him a trade; Borstal guided his ways –
When he wouldn't find work, his dole we still paid.
And lo! he repays our initial investment:

YOUTH DRUNK ON TIB STREET
IN ACT OF DIVESTMENT
(alleged)

I'm a friend dropping in, not a foe falling out,
Proudly reporting this evening about
An egregious Mancunian, deserving of praise:
It's the tale of a man of disciplined ways.
Eighteen years old, yet noble and fine –
He asked us for nothing; just gave all the time.
With origins humble, horizons so proud,
He stands out a mile from the rest of the crowd.
His face is clean-shaven, voice manly and gruff,
His profile patrician, and all that sob stuff.
When you hear what he did, you'll know hope lives on:

MAN BUILDS FREE TRADE HALL
WITH MATCHSTICKS AND GUM
(by Our Special Correspondent)

It's your old palsy-walsy, same as before,
Injected by hand through your very front door:

VICAR'S STRONG WORDS . . . QUEEN MOTHER'S NEW HAT . . .
PRINCE PHILIP AT LOWRY: BRING BACK THE CAT . . .
OLD TRAFFORD SHOCK . . . BUSINESSMAN'S BID . . .
SOCIALIST RUSE . . . PETROL SIX QUID . . .
WIDOWER'S VIGIL . . . UNION SCANDAL . . .
TORY MISGIVINGS . . . BELL BOOK AND CANDLE . . .
MINER'S RASH PAY CLAIM . . .YOUTH WENT BERSERK . . .
CHIEF CONSTABLE'S PLEDGE . . . FISH IN THE IRK . . .
TEACHERS REFUSE TO WORK WITHOUT PAY . . .
SOPHIE WESSEX GIVEN HER SAY . . .
ROD STEWART'S WOMEN (ad nauseam) . . .
SHARON STONE: IS SHE REALLY A MAN?
'Hey, look who's dead, ma . . . Only your age!'
BEAST OF BOLSOVER LOCKED IN A CAGE
'Who's had a baby? She's never wed!'
TWELVE FROM MOSS SIDE SLEPT IN ONE BED . . .
MP IN SAUNA . . . CUTS IN CHILD CARE . . .
QUEEN OF THE NETHERLANDS LOSING HER HEIR?

What? Feeling sleepy? (God, what a bore!)
Still, I've got your few bob – and your mind, what is more.

The Foresters Arms, corner Rochdale Road/Kingsbridge Road
(late Drinkwater Street), 1968

138

31

COLORADO

To *You Don't Say:* the *Daily Mess* (Northern Edition)

Sir,

Re: Page Three Girls

In view of your continuing appeal for what you refer to as "page three girls", which specifies too your preference for "the local, home-grown" variety, I must advise you that this reader (and advertiser) is unable to assist you in your quest, though I hasten to assure you that this failure on my part is not of my own design.

The problem is, I find, that all the girls of my acquaintance are without exception the kind of girls who say they would no more dream of cavorting before a camera in a state of undress for the titillation of whatever quota of armchair oglers you number amongst your readership than they would consider walking the streets to pay the rent.

And, despite my best endeavours on your behalf, these girls continue to walk and talk and breathe and have opinions of their own. They appear to have brains too, and insist on using them; they are possessed of feelings and are quite unafraid of letting them show. They work hard, or they play; they are homely or pretty; they have a good sense of humour or a sharp tongue and a temper to match. And they steadfastly remain mothers, daughters, sisters, nieces, and wives. They bath the baby, they enjoy the sun, they wear their hair long or short as it suits them, and they shop at Morrisons and ASDA.

I have no way of proving it to you, of course, but each and every one of them is headline news, despite remaining eminently unsuited to your purpose.

For instance, my sister says she regards herself as a person in her own right and she would consider it offensive in the extreme if a newspaper such as your own were to presume to treat her in much the same way as a side of beef in a butcher's window.

The one with the sharp tongue (I assure you we are only related by marriage) says: 'Send them a photo of our dog, Lulu – then they'll have a kennel-full!'

But my mother insists on having the last word. Mum says: 'It's a family show, *Daily Mess* – keep it clean!
Yours faithfully,

Byron Marlfield
(M/D, Colorado TV)

15 October 1986

Beech Mount Maternity Home,
corner Beech Mount / Rochdale Road, 1968

32

The Messengers

I personally – says Jim Harney – think the Pennine Way sees more fine weather than is ever generally allowed. But I also think that the day-tripper has a more controllable access to it, because he can study the meteorological reports at home overnight and strike while the Pennines are hot.

This, then, is just such a day (fine) and I such a tripper (day). So picture me, please, seven hundred feet or more above Horton-In-Ribblesdale en route to Hawes in Wensleydale. A true scorcher, it is, and I've forgotten my hat. So I cover my head with a hand towel, held in place with green twine. Sphinx-like, silent, with my back to the Cam End signpost, I have all Three Peaks in view – Whernside, Ingleborough, Penyghent – whilst to the north-east, if I turn my head a fraction and look towards Arkengarthdale in the far distance, I can feast my eyes on a great smooth sweep of moorland shimmering under the sun,

Bliss!

And so two o'clock rolls around on a glorious day in June and, along with the hour, a stray thought about a good friend of mine, Benny Wessenden, who just about now will be hanging up the blue tunic of his uniform and shutting the door of his locker at work on a shift that began at dawn in an area of the city where better days have been known, though not by the majority of its present-day inhabitants, the more visionary amongst which may not consider this too early an hour in which to check their household security arrangements against the coming of another night.

Then up out of the valley – Cam Houses behind them, Gearstones bound – come Dales Wayfarers, man and wife. Gasping for the cuppa said to be available at the farm in the valley, their faces had clouded – they tell me – when they had seen the note in the window.

'GONE TO MARKET,' it said, though their faces brightened, reading on: 'TEA/COFFEE IN KITCHEN – 50P PER CUP. PLEASE CLOSE THE DOOR WHEN YOU LEAVE.'

I'll say no more – says Jim Harney – nor did they, as they cheerio-ed towards Gearstones, and thence the source of the Ribble.

The Cintra Cinema (formerly the Palladium), then Gala Bingo Hall, Rochdale Road – also the Northern Club on the 1st floor), 1968

33

[EXTRACT] James T Harney's Unpublished Submissions
to the *Gruinard, Critique*

A Woman Called Intrepid
Henrietta Maria: the Intrepid Queen by Rosalind K Marshall
[Stemmer House, 1992, ISBN 088451187]

This is an absolute gem of a book and I own it quite by chance. It
was a happy choice of present from friends of mine who are not
historians and just happened to find themselves inspired one day
by a streak of beginners' luck. Glossy, superbly presented from
front cover to back, lavishly illustrated throughout from original
sources, empathetically written - I have read no better book in
recent years, and certainly no historical biography quite like it
since A. J. P. Taylor laid down his pen. It is a literary treasure
second to none.

Henrietta Maria (to allude to a curse, reputedly Oriental in
provenance) lived in interesting times. She was the daughter of a
king (Henri Quatre, the Huguenot who thought Paris 'worth a
Mass' and ended up paying for it with his life at the hands of an
assassin); she was the wife of a king (Charles I of England, who
utterly lost his chivalric heart to her and his head to the
Parliamentarians); and she was the mother of kings (Charles II,
who reigned for 25 post-Restoration years, and James II, who
learned no lessons from his father's decapitation and so lost the
monarchy for the House of Stuart). And this peerless volume tells
how she coped with her tribulations from first to last.

Even so, what must be recognised from the start is that it is
quite beyond the remit of Dr Marshall's masterpiece to supply
facts and figures sufficient to gain the reader a First in seventeenth
century Stuart studies – or even an A-Level Pass. But what this
book will do, and most effectively at that, is supply a sumptuously
panoramic background to more formal studies of the period, and in
a manner that renders them all the more readily comprehensible.
Because, for Henrietta Maria (daughter, wife, mother of kings,

Royalist fund raiser of armies and monies – in addition to being, in her marital role, quite frequently *enceinte*) all alarums tend to be 'off-', rather than 'on-stage'. And it is this unusual state of affairs which, in my estimation, lends the narrative such a refreshingly distinctive quasi-objective quality wherein the main protagonist in the story may well be far removed from the main action in any physical sense, yet is invariably caught up in it too, being so keenly affected by it on a more personal, emotional, feminine, and motherly level.

This Binky's lad by any chance? — Ed.

Bloomsbury Groupies
Mansfield by C K Stead
[Vintage, 2005, ISBN 0099468654]

'What a funny place this is!' says one of the Bloomsbury Group's hangers-on to Katherine Mansfield (*née* Kathleen Beauchamp, and one of the foremost modernist writers of her time). 'Such brilliant people saying such silly things.'

This comment just about sums up – not this superbly punctilious portrayal of Katherine Mansfield's creative years by fellow New Zealander and Mansfield scholar C. K. Stead – but the quite laughable, overweening inconsequentiality of a group of writers who, like the Algonquin Round Table in a different time and place, are so utterly convinced that the sun shines out of their art.

Various members of the group are sighted here together with assorted camp-followers: Virginia Woolf, D. H. Lawrence, Lady Ottoline Morell (on whom he based the man-eating Lady Chatterley), Aldous Huxley, Bertrand Russell, J. M. Keynes, and that other 'bugger' (as the aforementioned hanger-on viciously describes him), the insufferably bitchy Lytton Strachey – every one of them houseparting for England while the world goes to hell in a handcart.

'Last night . . .' trills the same silly also-ran,' we [took] a vote on whether the moon was a virgin or a harlot.'

Ah! time for Miss Mansfield to prove her mettle, I thought. How's she going to handle this latest bit of silliness?

Oh, dear! I was to be quickly disappointed. 'How did it come out?' says she.

Plus points: there are some wonderful set pieces here – D. H. Lawrence and his wife Frieda having a domestic spat, in the course of which they reveal themselves to be just as vain and childishly pathetic as lesser mortals having a domestic spat; and there's an achingly graphic depiction of the violent death in action during WWI of Katherine's beloved brother Leslie, and of Fred Goodyear being mortally wounded too.

Kathleen Mansfield can write like an angel when the fancy takes her, and when a quite different fancy takes her, she'll behave like a tramp. Consequently her lover of long-standing, John Middleton Murry, leads a veritable dog's life.

Leslie Beauchamp and Fred Goodyear apart, all the men of Katherine Mansfield's acquaintance are principled pacifists – the principle in question being that they are doggedly determined to dodge the draft. Meanwhile, the overwhelming majority of her women friends are ninnies in need of assistance to boil an egg or run a hot bath. In fairness, of course, it must be allowed that Katherine Mansfield is not one of these, though she does appear to have developed a brand of existentialism for her own personal use: 'I *can*,' you can almost hear her thinking, 'therefore I *shall!*'

And may the devil take the hindmost! Which means, of course, poor, long-suffering, affable, almost totally ineffectual John Middleton Murry, who is unlucky enough to be Katherine Mansfield's artistic and intellectual inferior – and saddled with her.

Name's familiar. He at St John's same time as Chas? — Ed.

The Abiding Masterpiece of the Billy Hopkins' Canon:
Kate's Story by Billy Hopkins
[Headline, 2002 ISBN 0747268525]

Kate's Story, the third book in the best-selling Hopkins family saga in which the author adopts the first person narrative voice of his own mother, is Billy Hopkins' finest literary achievement. This is not to denigrate his debut novel, *Our Kid*, in any way – or the rest of that hilarious sequence, culminating in the recently-published *Anything Goes*. But whereas the appeal of those other four books is of an immediately accessible kind for all and sundry – and quite rightly and understandably so! – *Kate's Story* is the sort of book (e.g. *Mrs Dalloway*, *The Great Gatsby*, *To Have and Have Not*, *The Grapes of Wrath*) that could not possibly have been written before its creator had succeeded in cutting his writer's teeth elsewhere. It is so much softer in tone, for one thing, and – given the serious, life-threatening vicissitudes in *fin-de-siècle* downtown Manchester that must be faced on a daily basis by the narrator and her loved ones (it opens in 1897, for example, with an eleven year old girl visiting her father's workplace, the cause of his premature and impending death) – its humour too is necessarily of the un-guffawing kind. But there is something else here too – a very particular something that, for me at any rate, marks *Kate's Story* out as the work of a master storyteller second to none.

John Braine used to say that you can't really call yourself a novelist until you've got three books under your belt. But what I think is worthy of even greater respect is when a male author so contrives things that he tells his tale with the voice of a woman. Which is what Billy Hopkins does in *Kate's Story*: he adopts the persona of his own mother.

Other authors have contrived a similar technique in the past – Anthony Burgess (aka Joseph Kell) with *One Hand Clapping*; Charles Portis with *True Grit*; David Storey with *Flight Into Camden*. But Billy Hopkins brings to the narrative of *Kate's Story* such thoroughgoing decency and unwavering sensitivity (as did Charles Portis with the masterly True Grit) that, all uncouth –

indeed, sham masculinity being set aside to that purpose, womankind as a whole will feel immediately at ease in his presence. Heck! she'll forget her narrator's a man!

And this, to my mind, makes *Kate's Story* by Billy Hopkins the most interesting and important social document penned by a writer of fiction since James Plunkett's Dublin-based *Strumpet City* back in the 1970s

It's not Binky's lad and Chas doesn't know him from Adam! – Pip

Burgessian Rhapsody
The Real Life of Anthony Burgess by Andrew Biswell
(Vintage, 2005, ISBN 0330481703)

Returned from holiday, where this book proved to be good company for a good few days, a dismissive and ill-informed review in today's *Fiducial Times* (London, 3 December, 2005) prompts me to spring to its defence. Because, though this new biography undoubtedly has its faults, there is no way in the world it is 'a monumental bore of a book', as critic, Antonia Tanhill, would have us believe. Personally, I found it to be a distinct improvement on Roger Lewis's recent contribution, which to my mind was top heavy with far too many chunks of Burgess's own extant prose, seemingly as space fillers. (Roger Lewis's only saving grace, it seems to me, was in suggesting that the Burgess persona is itself the author's most convincing fictional creation.

On the plus side, of course, this most recent biography is written by a Burgess *aficionado* (which Roger Lewis most certainly was not), so it is to Dr Biswell's credit that he chooses to reiterate this truism about Burgess that was first postulated by his biographical predecessor. (See page 306, where Deborah Regan, Burgess's literary agent since 1987 admits that: 'The distinction between life and fantasy was completely blurred.') In addition to this the author goes on to provide us with many fresh insights into

Burgess's life story via contributions from former colleagues, friends, acquaintances, and writers – Robert Graves' footnoted reminiscence of a remembered Burgessian critique being an absolute gem. And last but not least, the author is generous enough too to accord to L. W. Dever, Xaverian's long-serving history master of hallowed memory, the distinction of having introduced Burgess to the work of James Joyce, as opposed to his serving ignominiously and quite untruthfully (see *Little Wilson and Big God*) as a boozing partner pure and simple.

On the minus side, the author is occasionally remiss with regard to Mancunian geography. For example, it is the right bank of the River Irk, not Manchester General Cemetery, that is 'the western border of [Burgess's childhood stomping-ground] Harpurhey'. And Dr Biswell is mistaken too in referring to *the* (i.e. colloquially, there should be no definite article preceding) Lower Park Road, the location of Burgess's secondary school, Xaverian College. But in fairness, this is not so severe a fault as Antonia Tanhill's imagining Xaverian to be a Jesuit school. (Has Ms. Tanhill perhaps not actually read this book – or, indeed, Roger Lewis's book, to say nothing of Burgess's two volumes of autobiography?

Even so, it is surely demonstrably unsound for Dr Biswell to say (p.224) that, amongst the things that so appalled Burgess upon his return to the UK from Malaysia were 'sexual permissiveness' and 'a falling away of religious belief'. Because Burgess (by his own admission a phallic swordsman and apostate) cannot have it both ways – or can he?

And the author's narrative imprecision is occasionally irritating too. On the one hand, he gratuitously volunteers the actual plot number of Burgess's mother's grave in Manchester General Cemetery, whereas the location of Burgess's own resting-place in Monaco is not pinpointed in any way.

Was imprecision such as this the price of access to Burgess's widow, his second wife Liana? And is this the reason too why the untimely death of Burgess's (and Liana's) son, Paolo Andrea, is nowhere described as the suicide it most certainly was?

This last omission is particularly intriguing in view of

Burgess's own speculation (page 7) that: 'One becomes less able to give affection or take affection – because one never had this early filial experience'. So, did Burgess perhaps blame himself for a certain insensitivity in his relationship with Paolo Andrea? And, if so, is a further volume of Burgessian biography perhaps needed to elucidate the matter?

Even so, all things considered, I would maintain by way of conclusion – and paraphrasing Burgess's dedication of *The Clockwork Testament* (to Burt Lancaster, incidentally) that *The Real Life of Anthony Burgess* by Andrew Biswell ' . . . deserves to be read, deserves to be read.'

Ruddy Mancunians for Chrissake! Ignore 'em and they'll go away. By the bye, you and Fiona got anything planned for Cowes Week? – Ed.

34

The Hungry Years

When Clem Hardiker first took Yvonne Bateman home he was sixteen years of age and so was she, and he had her on her back in Andrew Road before they got as far as the ICI path. He could remember that he had laughed about it at the time and that Yvonne had laughed too, that he had thrown a snowball at the telegraph pole going down the hill on the left, that he had hit it full on, high up, that it was this that had made him lose his footing, and that he had broken his favourite 78 when they fell. The 78 was 'Searchin'' by the Coasters with 'Young Blood' on the flip-side, and Clem Hardiker replaced it with 'Problems' by the Everly Brothers, which was also on the London label and had 'Love of My Life' on the flip-side. But the new record wasn't half as good as the record he'd broken, not least because it was on 45.

His brother, Pete, two years his senior, had been annoyed with him at the time because 'Searchin'' was his record really. Pete had bought it at Mrs Wykes's record shop on Moston Lane some five years before and he and Clem had been giving it welly ever since.

Clem Hardiker did not see Yvonne Bateman for two years after that – if, that is, he had ever seen her at all.

Yvonne worked at Littlewoods on Piccadilly, and when she was eighteen she began working part-time behind the bar at the Old House at Home on the ICI path. Clem Hardiker would sometimes call in at the Old House at Home on his way home from work at Paul and Smart's on Bottomley Side. His cousin Derek would usually be in there at that time of day (Derek Keld, who worked at Barnes Green Post Office) and some of the other lads too. (One of them, Tosher Dermody would be on the gang from the Lecky that fed electricity cable into the Old House at Home for the first time in the summer of 1965. Prior to that gas mantles had been in use at The Old House at Home.) And soon, it got that way that all the lads would meet up at the Old House at Home, or the Millstone on the bend near Connolly's Cables, or the Fox in Blackley Village, not just after work, but before they would go out for the night at the weekend.

Every one of Clem Hardiker's mates was mad about Yvonne Bateman, and Derek Keld had been out with her once or twice. But Clem Hardiker never could see what they were on about. Okay, he'd taken her home that time, but the only thing he liked about Yvonne Bateman (though he kept this to himself, of course) was the way she'd fired Huge Jameson off when he came the Big I-Am like Huge Jameson usually did – and got away with it nine times out of ten too, being chocolate box good looking and a charmer to boot.

'I'll see you home when you're finished,' Huge Jameson told Yvonne one New Year's Eve, conveying to her a sense of blissful benediction in his tone of voice.

'Not if I see you first, you won't,' said Yvonne, dropping a dripping bar cloth into his lap to the hilarious amusement of his friends.

It would be 29 June, 1966, before Clem Hardiker saw Yvonne Bateman again. That is, it would be 29 June, 1966, before Clem Hardiker saw Yvonne Bateman properly as if for the first time, and saw too in his heart of hearts what Yvonne Bateman meant to him – Lord, what she must *be* to him or nevermore would he restful be.

And for the life of him, Clem Hardiker could not have said exactly what it was that suddenly enthralled him with the thought of Yvonne Bateman in that one anonymous instant in time in a room full of people and banter and cat calls and laughter and football chants and cheers.

Had the blue dress Yvonne was wearing that night perhaps lighted the blue of her eyes? Had the scales fallen from Clem's own eyes at last? Clem Hardiker would not have been able to say. But whatever it was that sparked it, the cold facts of the matter are these: at 7.13 pm precisely on 29 June, 1966, their eyes – Clem's eyes and Yvonne's eyes – locked for a moment like antlers, Yvonne looking up on a whim from where she was serving behind the bar, Clem turning from where he was overseeing a game of nine card Don; and Clem Hardiker never looked in other eyes again. From that moment in time Clem Hardiker ceased to be an apprentice engineer at Paul and Smart's, one of the lads, a lifelong

151

Manchester United supporter, a son, a grandson, a brother, a workmate, a neighbour, an acquaintance, a lad from Blackley, a Mancunian, an Englishman, a pal. These were the various hats he had worn at various times in the past, and which he now threw into the ring as he climbed into it after them, limbered up in his corner, and emerged on the bell (for last orders) as Clem Hardiker, lover to Yvonne Bateman.

By Royal Appointment too!

For Clem Hardiker had the key to Yvonne Bateman's heart before, metaphorically speaking, he had the key to his own front door. They were wed by the time they were twenty – Yvonne just. And Clem soon had her on her back in the Trevose Head guest house where they stayed on honeymoon in St Ives, in the upstairs front bedroom in the terraced house they bought on Goodman Street, in the front parlour, in the bathroom, in the guest room, and in the hall, the stairs, and on the landing on three separate occasions – the upshot being that five years down the line from their wedding day what had been two separate species combined as one, had now become six and it was time to take stock.

What finally brought it home to him was when Yvonne Hardiker (*née* Bateman) turned to him whilst they were watching *This Is Your Life* on TV one night (the subject of which was somebody they had never even heard of as usual, having been busy with other things) and told him:

'That ceiling needs doing, Clem.'

Clem looked up at the living-room ceiling, though not into his wallet. Because he already knew what was in his wallet – and there was plenty more of it where the wallet came from too: fresh air. Clem's wallet had been bought at a stall on Blackpool seafront when he and Yvonne were on a day trip from the Fox. 'Famous for fresh air and fun,' thought Clem Hardiker to himself. And in a way, it was only fair, Clem Hardiker thought too. Because he had certainly had the fun, so there was no way in the world he was going to miss out on the fresh air. Though why you need a wallet to store fresh air in, thought Clem Hardiker in his living-room that night too, is something that is known only to the God of Outward Appearances.

152

For five years Clem Hardiker had lived like a king. Watered and fed, he lived in clean surroundings, his clothes were washed and ironed for him, his family was welcomed, and certain of his friends were too. He had lived liked a king in other respects too, falling headlong into the yielding quicksand of Yvonnes's arms, plunging full fathom five into the blithe mysteries of that other world, tender and warm and loving and giving and true that is worth every penny a man can earn, and more. Worth every bit of it! Money spent as money should be spent; not frittered away, or thrown away, or gambled or hoarded or lost, but spent freely, proudly, generously – yes, unthinkingly too, every last penny of it like good coin of the realm should be spent, on the thing that you love.

You might love Man United, of course; plenty of his pals did. (Tosher Dermody never missed a match.) So they spent all they had on season tickets and away matches and memorabilia and associated gear. Hey, and fair play to 'em too, thought Clem. Or you might love travel to foreign parts – or clothes, or cars. Well, again, that was okay too, thought Clem. Yeah. You work for it, so spend it as you like. But Clem Hardiker loved Yvonne Hardiker (*née* Bateman), so that's where his money went, and that was certainly okay by him. *Christ*! (He caught his breath just thinking about her.) He loved her so much he could taste it – yes, taste it! Because sometimes when he thought of her, he would actually feel saliva spring onto his palate from some mysterious location adjacent to his wisdom teeth.

And by the time Clem's oppo, Olly Holwick, rendered the second finger of his right hand to the lathe in the back workbay at Paul and Smart's and was taken, bleeding profusely, into A&E at Crumpsall Hospital, Clem Hardiker knew the way forward.

'I'm goin' for gold this time,' Olly Holwick had said to Clem at the planning stage two weeks back. 'They coughed up two-fifty for me thumb three year ago. An' that was only the knuckle. What yer reckon this is worth?' And, so saying, Olly shoved his the second finger of his right hand in a vertical stabbing motion before Clem's eyes as if suggesting he should work it.

'What?'

'This, the finger. What'll I get for it, you reckon?'

'Dunno,' said Clem, his mind recoiling from the contemplated horror of it — from the horror of the projected accident, and from the unimaginable horror of planning to mutilate yourself for profit. 'Hunnerd,' said Clem.

'A *ton*?' said Olly, disgustedly. 'Told yer I got two fifty for the knuckle. Nah, I'll get mebbe a thou for this.'

'Oh, the *whole* finger,' said Clem Hardiker in the matter-of-fact manner of a quantity surveyor, simultaneously deciding he had had quite enough of his corned beef and Branston sauce sandwiches for one day.

But it's an ill wind that blows nobody good. And though Olly Holwick got only £300 for his finger due to contributory negligence, Clem Hardiker got Olly's part-time job waiting on at the North Parade on Victoria Avenue East.

The North Parade is a grill room nowadays, though there's still a vault and a lounge that attract a regular clientele. But when Clem Hardiker got the job waiting on at the North Parade it was a much busier boozer. There was no grill room in those days; the North Parade was a boozer pure and simple, as Clem Hardiker will tell you when he gets in the vault for the darts with son Joey on a Tuesday night still:

'It was a Wilsons' house, and in them days people'd make a bee-line for a Wilsons' house – hey, for Wilsons' mild at that! Course, that was before the accountants took over and Red Barreled all the good out of it that wasn't purely financial.'

The North Parade was so busy back in the early seventies when Clem Hardiker started working there, that it took half a dozen waiters to staff it on Friday, Saturday and Sunday nights, and just as many bar staff too.

'Eamonn Rochester was the landlord in them days,' Clem will tell you, 'and he never did a tap himself. Mind you, that's not to say he was the kind of lazy lummox who'll direct operations from the customers' side of the bar, gazin' through the bottom end of a dozen empty pint pots each night.'

No, Eamonn Rochester would be up there on the poop deck,

so to speak, next to the till, at the epicentre of operations behind the bar, arms folded in the main, hands fluttering outwards on occasion to accompany his verbal directions, his highly-polished shoes making a dancer's shuffle on the linoleum floor whenever he'd turn his attention in a 360 degree angle to encompass four of the North Parade's five outlets for Wilsons' product – the lounge, the concert room, the vault, and the snug. (The off-licence Eamonn would visit personally whenever he was summoned to do so by means of a bell's being rung.)

Eamonn was never ever joined behind the bar by Mrs Rochester – that is, by Mrs Nutter (to give her her official married name), the name Rochester having been bestowed on them by the man from Colorado TV ('the darkie', as Jim Jordan in the vault called him), though there were rumours that there *was* a Mrs Rochester – upstairs, in the living accommodation, keeping house and keeping mum. For Mrs Eamonn Nutter was not mad, despite her married name, and she was certainly not pyrotechnically inclined as her nickname might suggest. 'Well, not so far, at least', said Jim Jordan in the vault to the man from Colorado TV who had given Eamonn the name Rochester – that same man, incidentally, who nearly thirty years in the future (in April, 1998, to be exact) would come up with the readies to buy the North Parade off the brewery, kick out the drugs-involved reprobate (not Eamonn: Eamonn had retired to Blackpool by that time) who had run it into the ground, completely refurbish the place, stick in a spanking brand new kitchen, and install his brother, Pearson Marlfield, as pub manager, and brother Winston – long-serving member of Brian Hughes' local boxing stable – as the restaurant manager.

Eamonn Rochester started Clem Hardiker on on the third Sunday in July. 'Not too busy,' said Eamonn, 'but busy enough. Give you a chance to find your feet.'

And so saying, he gave Clem a £2 float (to be returned at the end of the night) and set him loose on the snug where Clem milk-stouted it, cream-sherried it, and just-half-a-pinted it till half past ten at night, which was the early closing time that Mr Lloyd George had imposed on the British public over half a century before when he was at a loss as to how he might best direct the war effort and thought early closing might put the great British public in a mind to do it for him.

Clem Hardiker did okay. He earned £1 for his night's work (eight o'clock till half past ten) and, after paying Eamonn the £2 float back, he found he had another 50p in tips. Eamonn took 5p off him for the 'crash fund' and 5p for the bar staff, so Clem Hardiker was £1.40 to the good. He had been bloodied as a waiter, he had handled the tray and the money, and better still he had learned the infallible subtractive technique of supplementary addition:

'£3.60, and you gave me – a fiver, wasn't it, love? £3.80, £4, £4.50, £5. Thanks very much.'

Clem Hardiker waited on at the North Parade four nights a week after that, earning himself £4 a week and tips, and Eamonn booked him down as working an extra night that he didn't work, so the extra night paid Clem's tax. As Jim Jordan in the vault said, just before the Inland Revenue closed his butcher's shop down: 'Why pull your tripes out for the Chancellor? Bastard wouldn't pull 'em out for you.'

That £4 a week plus tips came in handy, especially with the tips on top – and the tips got better. After two weeks on the snug Clem was moved to the busier lounge and his tips improved. And when he was promoted to the concert room, where on Friday, Saturday and Sunday nights four experienced waiters were kept busy all night, Clem Hardiker was doing very nicely indeed. At the end of a busy Saturday night he would regularly make £3, including tips.

'And I never take more than a tanner,' he told Yvonne, who sometimes joined him on a Sunday evening if a baby sitter could be found.

Moneywise, Christmas was a dream. Come Christmas, Clem Hardiker had been working at the North Parade for five months and he had been saving his money. So he and Yvonne hit the January sales.

They bought a new TV from Comet in Castleton, and outfits for the kids from Broadbent's in Middleton, and decorated and carpeted the house, courtesy of Nugent's at the corner of Mary

Street and Mr Cavanagh on Moston Lane, and got the new kitchen Yvonne had been after from di Lusso in Blackley Village, and booked a holiday for Whitsun in Magaluf. Clem took one weekend off in February and the six of them stayed at a B&B in Blackpool. Of course, in the rapture of spending money they had never previously possessed, they overspent. Still, Clem was in work and Yvonne and the kids were happy.

Clem Hardiker went back to the North Parade on the Monday after he got back from Magaluf and got Eamonn Rochester to give him an extra night to pay off his debts. Clem Hardiker was now doing Monday, Tuesday, Friday, Saturday, and Sunday nights, and he was earning £13.50, sometimes £15, a week part-time, tax paid, plus a free drink every night, plus the very best pint of Wilsons' ale known to man.

It was a good pint of beer at the North Parade anyway (or *ale*, rather, as Wilsons so described its product). But for the waiters' drinks Eamonn would order the sparklets on the pumps to be tightened right up and, aerated thus, the waiters' drinks were given an extra, very palatable edge. Very palatable indeed, though Clem Hardiker never overdid it. He drank two pints a night because he was driving, never more. Ten pints a week, maybe another ten, if they called in on one or two of his nights off and Yvonne was driving – twenty pints a week, his intake now measurable by the gallon. Before that he would have had maybe four pints a week in total. Clem Hardiker had his first accident coming home from the North Parade on the Monday before his second Christmas there.

'All right, I'd had three pints that night,' Clem confided to his cousin, Derek Keld, 'not my normal two. I'd already had my quota when Olly Holwick bowls in at last orders and sticks a pint in front of us; and what is a boy to do but . . .' At which point Clem Hardiker made a supping motion, raising a cupped right hand to his lips and tilting his eyes upwards to encompass the Christmas decorations, a light fitting and an unnecessary flypaper that hung from the ceiling of the vault of the Old House at Home.

It wasn't much of an accident, but it was enough. Three hundred yards or so from the North Parade, negotiating the Gardeners Arms roundabout as he was going home that night,

Clem Hardiker lost control of his FB Victor saloon with the result that the off side front wheel mounted the roundabout. Luckily, no one was hurt and the police weren't about. Clem was more surprised than shaken. But the bill for repairs cost him three weeks' money. When Clem had the car towed in to Hillier Street Garage, Jim Phillips told him the off side front suspension had gone – and the Monday night of the accident Clem had had to walk home in the rain, so he ruined his suit and his best shoes. Then he overslept because he was late home, was late for work the next morning, and cursed his bad luck all day. But he had the car back on the road by the following Monday. He had his second accident around Easter time, and again he was driving home from the pub.

He had driven along Victoria Avenue East, done a right on to Lightbowne Road at the Gardeners Arms, swung right on to Nuthurst Road at Broadhurst Fields, then left on to Moston Lane, going home. It was after midnight and he'd had two pints after the death. But again Clem was lucky in that there was nothing else on the road, when for some reason unknown to Clem, and ever afterwards claimed as such by him, instead of turning where he should have turned (that is, right on to Goodman Street from Moston Lane) he took the turning immediately before Goodman Street on to Clough Road.

Well, almost.

Because no sooner had he completed this manoeuvre than 'the car took on a life of its own', Clem Hardiker always said, and smashed into the wall of Darbyshire's tyre bay, peeling some masonry paint off the wall and six weeks money off Clem Hardiker's wad: the price of an off-side front wing, headlight, side light and assorted accessories from that Polish chap (Clem never did get his name right) who had the body shop near the Conservative Club in Blackley Village. Clem Hardiker managed to limp home in the car that night, tootling gingerly along Clough Road and down Lewis Avenue and, apart from the freebie Eamonn Rochester let him have when he was waiting on, Clem immediately gave up drinking.

He moved the Victor on at Whitsun and got the first thing that came to hand, an E reg Farina line Cambridge estate in a Rose Taupe that never buffed to a shine all the time he had it. To celebrate he took two weeks off from the pub and took Yvonne and the kids on day trips to Blackpool, Southport, New Brighton, and Hollingworth Lake (or, 'Hollywood Flake', as son Joey insisted on calling it), where they dined like royalty on fish, chips and peas at Mr Thomas's. Then it was back to work for Clem.

Things had perked up a bit at Paul and Smart's by now and Clem would very often get a Saturday or a Sunday, and sometimes a Saturday *and* a Sunday – and if overtime was offered at Paul and Smart's you had to take it or you would never be offered overtime again. So, when Clem worked a seven day week and five nights at the North Parade he was on very good money indeed, but he was working a 72 hour week. Plenty of cab drivers – Clem knew, because his brother, Pete, drove for Line Bunratty on B-Line – plenty of cabbies worked a 72 hour week, but there was a difference, and it was this: Clem Hardiker worked a 72 hour week on his feet, not sitting on his backside on the rank half the time, reading the newsprint off the *Daily Mess* and smoking his way through sixty Benson and Hedges cigarettes a day.

The third crash shook him up more than he would have imagined possible.

It was the Monday of the September holidays, that throw-back of a bacchanal which, in those days, the 1970s, affected the town of Oldham and surrounding towns that followed its lead. Thus it was a custom of long-standing that, no sooner had all the kids gone back to school in September than it was time for a break from work – hence the September holiday. And being within a stone's throw of the Chadderton-Oldham, boundary, the North Parade was affected by the September holiday too.

The concert room was packed that Monday night in September, though no artiste was scheduled. What the three waiters serving the concert room faced on this occasion was an auditorium filled with seated boozers at formica topped tables (if you wanted to stand around, getting under people's feet, Eamonn Rochester would direct you to the vault), who were listening (when sporadic lulls in the conversation would permit this) to pop music piped through speakers in each of the four corners of the room. In retrospect, Clem Hardiker would remember four things about the Monday night in question, and ruefully at that.

First of all, when Clem turned up at the concert room at the North Parade at eight o'clock that night he found a fourth waiter, Frank Leitrim, had failed to turn up at all; secondly, as a consequence of Frank Leitrim's absence, each of the other three waiters was expected to accommodate a third of Frank's normal ration of tables in addition to his personal quota; thirdly, immediately before Clem Hardiker fell, John Travolta and Olivia Newton-John could be heard, singing 'You're The One That I Want'; and, fourthly, in the total silence that lasted for all of five seconds whilst he, Clem Hardiker, was lying flat on his back after a spectacular fall with a tray of drinks at 10.22pm that evening, the Commodores, with Lionel Ritchie's voice to the fore, were quietly insisting that someone was 'Three Times A Lady'.

Eamonn Rochester was very good about it.

'Look, you're a good lad, Clem,' he told Clem privately in the aftermath of the crash whilst Clem was trying, with a wet bar cloth and little success, to get the Bleeding Heart stain (Cherry Brandy and Advocaat) out of his pants. 'One of the best. So, take some time off, will you? Take her to the hallucinations.' Eamonn invariably substituted this word for 'illuminations', meaning Blackpool Illuminations, so nobody laughed any more; certainly, no one was laughing now with all the glass and beery gunginess underfoot in the bar area, two waiters short, and less than five minutes to go till last orders. 'Bit of a break for the both of you. Take the kids, you wannoo, though I'd leave 'em at home, it was me. Hallucinations, bit of sea air, plenny to eat and drink, come back refreshed. Take a month, you like. Always a job for you here, Clem. You know that.'

Clem Hardiker did a bit better than a trip to Blackpool Illuminations. With seventy-two non-drinking, non-smoking hours work a week under his belt during the last – what was it now? – six, seven months or so, Clem Hardiker and Yvonne had a fair amount in the bank, and so they adjourned to Gran Canaria during the first week in October, leaving the four kids with Yvonne's mother, and £2,000 on deposit with the Avon & Test Building Society.

Clem and Yvonne had a ball.

One week later – wined, dined, sun-tanned and rested, tour-guided and belly-laughed, seven pounds heavier each of them, they arrived back at Manchester Airport where a Citicars taxi was waiting to whisk them back home again – their only worries in the whole wide world being chronological. (Clem) Would he (off the wagon for the duration of the holiday) be in time to catch last orders at the North Parade? And (Yvonne) had she made a correct calculation with regard to her biological clock?

The baby, a little girl, the fifth Bateman-Hardiker progeny, with lovely blue eyes like Yvonne and what son Joey, aged nine, termed 'a Beatle haircut with an hole in it, like you, dad', was born in July, 1979, in St Mary's Hospital, Manchester.

Living so near to Manchester District Hospital, St Mary's had not been Yvonne's first hospital of choice, but she had ended up at St Mary's very early on.

'How many've you got now?' were (Yvonne said) the first words out of the gynaecologist's mouth when she arrived at the Ante-Natal Clinic at Crumpsall. 'Four, eh? Well, you can't keep going on like this!'

Nobody was more aware than Yvonne Hardiker that she could not keep 'going on like this' – and on financial grounds alone. But, quite apart from that, she did not consider it much of a welcome to an Ante-Natal Clinic, nor did she appreciate the gynaecologist's alluding to the new life inside her as a 'going on'. Besides, Yvonne Hardiker had no intention of submitting herself to the attentions of a doctor who might possibly be able to put a hex on the new baby with the look in his eyes.

As she said to Clem when she got back home: 'You don't ask a tomcat's advice about haddock; there's only one thing he knows!'

'Two,' said Clem, goosing her in an effort to cheer her up as she inclined herself to fill the washing machine for the third time that week.

Yvonne booked herself into St Mary's the following week,

and never regretted she had done so even though her ante-natal appointments would entail her having to get two buses on occasion whenever the car might be unavailable due to breakdown or some other exigency.

'Shop!' was the welcome Yvonne received from the gynaecologist at St Mary's. This – followed up with a cheery smile, a business-like rubbing of the hands, as if making preparations to shell another pea, and a bustling, matter-of-fact aura amongst the hospital staff gathered around him – were indicative, Yvonne felt, of sincerity, safety, and a warm welcome to the world.

Yvonne's confinement and the delivery – 'within sight of Maine Road floodlights,' as she pointed out to Clem's 'Ah well, she'll probably get over that' – were an unmitigated success, Clem turning up for his first visit with the other four kids. (They were doing this very carefully indeed, Yvonne and Clem – presents for each of the four kids 'from the baby'; all of them to be included in the great bringing home of the baby.) The only downside (on the occasion of that first visit) being the sweltering temperature in the ward when someone in one of the private rooms was found to have left a window wide open to a squally night, sending a wrong signal to the heating thermostat.

Clem got the kids up bright and early (Joey, Carole, Holly, and Jamie) to make sure everything was as it should be at their house on Goodman Street (not theirs for very much longer now: they'd need three bedrooms with three girls and two boys), and then he had taken them down to town for breakfast at Rowntree's in the Arndale Centre where Lou opened at 8 am on the dot, seven days a week, and the five of them then breakfasted – breakfast, no sausage, extra bacon for Clem; two breakfasts; two lots of toasted tea cakes; one coffee; four orange juices; six rounds of toast; a Kit-Kat; a Club biscuit; a vanilla; a Bakewell tart; another coffee for Clem – and they were on their way to pick up Yvonne and the new baby from the hospital shortly after nine o'clock.

There weren't many people at St Mary's at that time of day. So, it was relatively easy to have Yvonne and the new baby ensconced in the rear seat of the Cambridge estate by a quarter to ten with the four kids, aged four to eight years old squeezed in around her. By half past eleven they were home, and Clem was out on the road again within the hour, looking for a replacement clutch – the damned thing had been slipping all the way back from Ardwick Green roundabout to Goodman Street. That same evening he was back on the pub.

'You're not doing five nights, no,' Eamonn Rochester told him. 'Do the four and have done. I'll let you have three good uns, Friday through Sunday, pick t'other for yourself. But you're not doing five. You'll kill yourself, or you'll crock yourself, and neither one of them's any good to me.'

Clem realised Eamonn was right, and, in a way, he was glad to lose that fifth night. Besides, having the three weekend nights would probably put him on the same money anyway. None of the other waiters had that sort of a deal with Eamonn. The norm was two nights midweek and two at the weekend, which was only fair. But Clem was a sort of senior waiter by now – if there can be said to be any such thing in the realm of part-time work. Clem Hardiker was empowered to take minor policy decisions when Eamonn wasn't there, to change the barrels, to stand in for Eamonn behind the bar, to sort out the bar snacks. Crisps, nuts, savoury bites, biscuits and cheese, chocolate. (Some of the lads out of the vault would watch the racing or the football on TV of a Saturday afternoon and other odd times and would not have been home for a meal after work).

Clem picked most of these comestibles up for Eamonn at Yankee Mantle in Hollinwood. There was no pay for doing so, but Clem enjoyed it – keeping abreast of new lines that came in and any deals that were on offer. Besides, the North Parade's card gave him access to Yankee Mantle for his own needs too, and with five growing kids at home and a wife who was busy with them morning, noon and night (as she said) – this was the year of illnesses and hospitalizations (mumps, rubella, chicken pox, a case of pneumonia) – there were always plenty of takers for Yankee Mantle's stock in trade at the little house on Goodman Street and at the slightly larger house they moved to on Westleigh Street before the year was out. Easter was no problem for Clem Hardiker either with his purchase of six Easter eggs discounted via Yankee Mantle. He even started buying in the pies and pasties for Eamonn at a baker's outlet on Bury Market: meat and potato, meat, Cornish pasties, beef and onion, cheese and onion. He'd run up to Bury on market days (Wednesday, Friday, or Saturday: you could always find somewhere to park free at Bury), get whatever was needed, and drop it back at the pub when it opened.

'Hey up,' Eamonn would go, 'make way for Monty Pie-son!' Eamonn Rochester said this every time Clem turned up with the baker's tray, said it fifty times a year; and fifty times a year, someone would laugh

A similar order, though proportionately less, would go home with Clem. He got trade price for the bulk order plus a little extra to sweeten it because the order was a regular, week by week order, and Eamonn Rochester would invariably push the sweetener Clem's way. The Hardikers had a chest freezer by now, though seven Hardiker mouths ensured the freezer was never full for long.

'Continuity,' said Clem Hardiker, philosophising about the catering trade, 'that's the name of the game. What's the point of having a good line if you've not got it the next time Fanny Fernackerpan wants it? She might go elsewhere, and you stand the chance of losing her custom for good then.'

'Hey, listen Monty Pie-son!' said Jim Jordan in the vault, hearing this.

'Drink up and get out,' said Clem, coldly. (Eamonn was at York Races for the day.) 'It's half past eleven – time you wasn't with me; so, piss off, yer twat!'

Clem would share a joke with anyone, even when the joke was on himself. But tonight Clem had felt his age.

Non-smoking, non-drinking (apart from the staff freebie and nights out with Yvonne), Clem was two stones overweight by this time. The years of boozing had shoved the weight on him, the years of non-smoking had kept it *in situ*; and his life-style was far too active for somebody who was seriously overweight: Paul and Smart's – a minimum of forty-eight hours a week, on the pub four nights (four nights that Eamonn Rochester still refused to allow him to increase to five), with three of those four nights being busy nights. Clem Hardiker was active with a capital A.

But that night, a Saturday night, he had only done the bar, so he did hardly any rushing about. Strange that he should feel it then, thought Clem. Okay, so he had come on earlier than usual that evening, but all he had done was stock up by means of the dumb waiter, make sure everything was in order with regard to snacks and comestibles, and stand there like King Dick all night, serving on occasion, but only when the bar staff were busy elsewhere. But, come closing time, he was glad of the opportunity to sit down and eat his pasty. It was the last pasty left in the warm cabinet. They were a popular line.

'Last one. Anyone want it?' asked Clem Hardiker, pretending to wipe his nose on it in a motion reminiscent of Larry Adler playing the harmonica. He bit into the pasty, devoured it in four mouthfuls. Maybe book a night off, thought Clem.

He booked a night off – booked a regular night off; dropped down to three nights on the pub. Tried to pace himself a bit better. Clem Hardiker was fourteen and a half stone now: the years of boozing and subsequent comfort eating had taken their toll. When he and Yvonne got wed he had been exactly ten stone in weight in his reefer on the scales in the Old House at Home, boozed up on a Saturday night. The extra sixty pounds were getting to be too much to carry around. Heck, thought Clem – he had worked part-time in Pollard's grocer's shop next door but one to the Alliance when he was a kid – sixty pounds was more than two packs of sugar! (The two-pound bags of Tate and Lyle sugar came packed in fourteens.) Those twenty-eight pound packs of sugar were some weight, he had always thought. Not a forfeit you'd accept with good grace at the start of a brisk jog for the bus, never mind a marathon that entailed going to work three hundred days a year and waiting on at the North Parade for two hundred nights.

But the weight stayed with him. If anything – with Clem having the extra night off from the pub – the weight problem got worse. He was up to fifteen stone before he went for it, going down to twelve stone on a strict calorie-controlled diet over six months in 1982, screaming every time an extra lettuce leaf hit his plate Then just before Easter, he did a fortnight on the Cabbage Soup Diet he'd heard about, and he reached eleven stone seven.

Not bad, boy, Clem Hardiker congratulated himself, diving into a celebratory bash on the kids' Easter eggs, putting half a stone on in three days, and shooting up to twelve stone again. Hey, but still not bad, Clem thought. Then Clem Hardiker lost another few ounces at a stroke when he lost his left index finger in an accident at work.

Best practice at Paul and Smart's dictated that, when working at the lathe metal swarf was to be removed by means of a metal bar. Some of the lads ignored the rule, being adept at their trade and somewhat cavalier in their attitude to metal swarf. Half the time they simply ignored the rule for the pleasure of hearing Arthur Rishworth, the foreman, rant and rave.

'Damn, blast and bugger it!' Arthur would go whenever he saw any of them standing up to the lathe, removing metal swarf by hand. 'How many times have I got to tell you? That's not the way we do it here, and we never have. The next man-jack of yous I find at it don't get no overtime at the weekend – just like he won't get no compo off Paul and Smart's if he loses a finger. Because I'll make damned sure he don't.'

The lads would laugh then – old Arthur, they'd say to one another, always going on with himself. Not that any of them disliked Arthur (sound as a pound, Arthur Rishworth – they'd say this too); they just liked to hear him ranting and raving. And Clem Hardiker laughed with the best of them, though as a rule Clem Hardiker would remove metal swarf with a metal rule. But not on the Friday after Easter.

Clem Hardiker didn't want to work the weekend – he wanted to go fishing with his brother Pete, up at Slattocks. There were crayfish in the ponds at Slattocks, the last remnant, so it was said, of the internment camp that was there during the war, when the ponds had been stocked with crayfish for consumption in the officers' mess. If Clem got the weekend off he could spend Saturday morning up at Slattocks, take Yvonne out on the Saturday night, have a lie in on the Sunday, go up to Hollingworth Lake with her and the kids on Sunday afternoon, and maybe have a meal at the Beach or the Fish.

'You ever tried the Fish?' Clem Hardiker asked Johnny Redbrook, meaning the Fisherman's Rest at Hollingworth Lake.

But before Johnny Redbrook had time to shout back over the noise of the lathes, Clem Hardiker saw Arthur Rishworth approaching on his tour of inspection and, working some alloy at the lathe, Clem went for it. Right under Arthur Rishworth's eagle eye he took his left index finger to some metal swarf, hoping to take the weekend off, and took his finger off as well. The metal swarf remained exactly where it was – a bloody crimson shade now – as Clem Hardicker keeled over and hit the floor in a dead faint.

He soon came round, of course. Johnny Redbrook saw to that, and Johnny Redbrook cast about for Clem's finger too. But Arthur Rishworth already had it. Arthur Rishworth laid Clem Hardiker's detached index finger on a folded piece of toilet tissue in a Golden Virginia tobacco tin and the Golden Virginia tobacco tin and its contents accompanied Clem Hardiker to a waiting ambulance that whisked him to Wythenshawe Hospital where vain attempts were made to re-unite finger and man.

All was not lost at Paul and Smart's that afternoon, however. For two young apprentices learned that same afternoon never to mess about with metal swarf when, acting on the principle that actions speak louder than words, Arthur Rishworth made damned sure they learned this lesson by having them personally, individually, and consecutively open the Golden Virginia tobacco tin under the impression that he was offering them a smoke.

'Sometimes,' said Arthur Rishworth to his wife that night, 'you've gotta be cruel to be kind. And I'm gonna cruel the bugger too, Edie, you just see if I don't. Hardiker'll get no compo from Paul and Smart's. I'll see to that, the silly bugger. Thought he had a bit more about him, Clem. Just goes to show, you never can tell.'

In Clem Hardiker's case attempts at microsurgery were unsuccessful, though the specialist did his best for him. (Clem and Yvonne never did get his name straight; the best stab they had at it was Bandy Striker, though they had the good sense to keep this to themselves). Dr B was an expert in the field of microsurgery, having made his way to this country via hospitals in Tokyo, Cape Town, and upstate New York.

'Best we address the problem with traditional methods, I think,' said Dr B, referring Clem Hardiker to North Manchester General Hospital since appointments there would be easier to keep with its being nearer to the Hardiker's home address.

So, after travelling by ambulance from Wythenshawe to Crumpsall, Clem had his wound dressed, and was kept in overnight for observation. Yvonne picked him up in the Cambridge estate the next day at noon, and by three o'clock that same afternoon – the kids being at school, the house being warm and peaceful, and there having been no domestic interruptions to speak of – by three o'clock that same afternoon, Yvonne Hardiker (*née* Bateman) had further cause to be concerned about her biological clock.

Yvonne was not the only one who was concerned. Clem Hardiker was concerned too – and quite specifically for reasons of finance. There could be no question of his going back to Paul and Smart's for the time being. So he was on short time to begin with. Also, there was not much chance of his claiming compensation for the accident because Paul and Smart's had refused point blank, management having been fully appraised of the circumstances by Arthur Rishworth.

In due course Clem Hardiker consulted his union representative, and the union submitted an appeal on Clem's behalf. But it was a half-hearted sort of appeal at best, Clem always felt, since it was generally accepted by all concerned (even the workforce) that Clem Hardiker's accident was not work-related in any proper sense of the term: He'd come a cropper due to his own stupidity. Of course, the lads had a whip-round for him, and they passed a name card round the canteen and £206 was raised, which they had Arthur Rishworth take round to Clem's house on Westleigh Street on the Friday before Whit.

Clem sensed Arthur's embarrassment as soon as he opened the front door and found him standing there with the cheque in his hands on that Friday evening after work.

'Come in, Arthur. It's good of you to call,' said Clem, the noise of the Scooby Doo programme the kids were watching on the TV floating through from the living room behind him. 'I'll stick the kettle on. We're not eating yet. Missis has just popped out to Asda.'

Arthur Rishworth looked a bit uncertain, uncomfortable even.

'Oh, come in, for God's sake,' said Clem, inspecting the cheque which Arthur proferred. 'If anyone should be embarrassed, it's me. Two hunnerd . . . two hunnerd and six. Christ, it's more than decent of the lads. Oh, I know what you've been up to, Arthur. But I can't say you didn't warn us, can I? I mean, I can't blame a man for being true to his word, can I now?'

'Well, it's very good of you to see it like that, lad,' said Arthur Rishworth. 'I'm responsible for the lot of yous, you know, not just you. That's what it's all about, lad. Okay, maybe I could've got you a bit of pay-out. But just suppose it'd been at the cost of some other young lad's fingers. They'll maybe take note now.' Arthur had remained standing in the hallway, and stood back at this point to let Yvonne come through from the front door with her shopping.

'Good eve-ning, Mr Rish-worth,' said Yvonne distantly, clipping her words, not pausing to converse with either of the two men as she pushed her way between them with her bags of shopping in her hands.

'I'll get that cuppa another time,' said Arthur Rishworth, who knew where he wasn't wanted. 'If you're not back in a fortnight, I'll maybe pop round again.' Arthur paused momentarily as he stepped out on to the street. Then, turning, he reached quickly across, shoved something in Clem's breast pocket, and was instantly away.

The twenty pound note was folded in three, the creases sharp, the note being fresh from the Midland Bank at the corner of Waterloo Road that dinnertime. Not that Edith Rishworth would ever feel the pinch of her husband's charitable impulse. Arthur Rishworth would not be going to Barnes Green Club, as he usually did, until four Friday nights had passed. His excuse, reiterated on each of those four Friday nights, would be that he didn't know what was the matter with him nowadays, Edie. He felt 'really tired', he did. It must be that order they were getting together for Saudi, knackering it was: reckoned he'd sleep without a few pints inside him tonight, Edie.

'Yvonne, he gimme . . . he gimme twenny quid on top of the cheque,' said Clem, going through to the kitchen. 'I wish you'd . . .'

'Oh, aye?' said Yvonne, her tone of voice indicating total disinterest. It was as if she were not even listening to him. She glanced round at him once, almost unseeing, then continued stowing the groceries in the kitchen cupboard.

'*What*? What're you looking at?

'Dunno. It's not got a label on it.'

Being on short time at Paul and Smart's was not the end of Clem Hardiker's money worries in the six months remaining before the sixth child was born. He was finished as a waiter too. Because Clem very soon discovered he could no longer carry a tray in the way that is a waiter's wont – fingers spread a-wide beneath the base of the tray to support a balanced load of pots, glasses, and bottles, with the heavier gear to the centre.

'Fin-*ee*!' as Clem Hardiker said resignedly to Eamonn Rochester one evening towards the end of the year.

Nor was he any good on the bar, except for the odd time in a supervisory capacity when Eamonn was maybe on a trip to the races or at a family wedding or whatever. Being right-handed, Clem needed to hold a pint pot in his left hand whilst working the pump with his right, and try as he might, he could not get used to holding the handle of the pint pot with the second finger of his left hand.

'What're we gonna do?' he asked Yvonne.

'I don't know what *you're* gonna do,' said Yvonne, failing to add: 'And I don't care' – her tone of voice making this quite unnecessary. 'But I know what *I'm* gonna do. I'm gonna *have* another baby.'

Yvonne had the baby in the December, their sixth child, another girl. Two boys, four girls: the girls had won, Yvonne decided unilaterally. Again she had the baby at St Mary's, though on this occasion the homecoming was very different.

Clem and the kids were in their starting blocks as usual. The five kids had already visited the hospital and had each received a present from the baby, as was Clem and Yvonne Hardiker's custom. But when Clem said they'd be back in the morning to pick the two of them up – Yvonne and the baby, Yvonne said to let them go in to school. It was school photographs tomorrow anyway, she said. Yvonne would get a taxi.

Yvonne did not get a taxi. The sister on Yvonne's ward would not hear of it. If Mrs Hardiker wanted to get a taxi, well, fine, but Mr Hardiker must be in that taxi. No way was sister going to release one of her ladies, unaccompanied, whilst a related male was available to attend her. In this, sister was only adding her entreaties to Clem Hardiker's own, but it was sister's word that carried the day, not Clem's – and the four older children went in to school as usual. The Cambridge estate, with Clem Hardiker at the wheel, accompanied by baby number five in the back seat, arrived at St Mary's hospital mid-morning and took Yvonne Hardiker and baby number six (Roslyn) home.

Clem Hardiker had £1500 in the Avon & Test Building Society at the time. The mortgage payments were up to date, the car was paid for (maybe it was time to get a newer one – he liked the look of the Avenger: he'd seen one in Oscar Boniecki's showroom on Chapel Street, Salford – but that could wait), he owed nothing on the furniture or the fitted kitchen (maybe the bathroom could use a facelift – he fancied some of that stuff he'd seen in Texas on Great Ancoats Street – but that, too, could wait), his six kids were in good health and four were in school, and he had a wife he had been crazy about from day one, but . . . who – he was soon to discover – now slept with him only in the somnolent sense of the word.

For a full twelve months after they brought the sixth child Roslyn, home from the hospital, Yvonne Hardiker was constantly 'sore', 'dry', 'headachy', 'tired', not inclined towards any wakeful bedtime activity, or fast asleep when Clem climbed into bed. Thereafter, Yvonne's interest in such matters was tepid at best, functional only, and limited to once weekly, if that – and, from preference (Yvonne's) only on the night before she'd be washing the bedsheets next day anyway. Almost overnight, it occurred to Clem, he had become a married man with all the responsibilities of a married man (which he continued to undertake with a willing heart), yet with regard to the girl he loved (he still thought of her as a girl – and he still loved her as he had loved that girl) he retained all the conjugal rights of an anchorite.

He tried to deal with the situation on a day to day basis. As far as he could see this was the only thing he could do. What was the point of arguing about it? Where would that get him? What use (to employ an infelicitous term) was a pressed man in sexual congress? Daily (or, rather, nightly), Clem Hardiker continued to try, continued to hope for Yvonne's present mood to pass, to hope for better things – for a return to the status quo, for Yvonne's arms to open to him lovingly as they had opened to him in the past. But in this, he hoped in vain.

The days became weeks, the weeks became months, the months became years. And there never was a return to the status quo. Because there were eight Hardikers now, and seven of those Hardikers were constantly vying for Yvonne's attention, and Clem just happened to be the one who continued to lose out – the one who, in losing out, could most certainly be prevented from giving Yvonne the problem of a ninth Hardiker to cope with. He continued to live in hope, of course, that something would spark Yvonne's remembrance of how things had once been with them, what they had meant to each other. How he yearned for a return to the special relationship that had been their very own. But, for Clem Hardiker and Yvonne Hardiker (*née* Bateman), this was not to be. All his hopes were dreamworld hopes. For something had died in Yvonne, something without which no reconciliation would ever be permitted to come about – something without which reconciliation was quite impossible.

For Yvonne's part it was as if no special relationship had ever existed, as if it were something that was not even a shared memory between them. Birthday presents continued to be exchanged, Christmas presents too, and every year in February there would be a Valentine gift from Clem – just as there would be no reciprocal reaction from Yvonne other than a civil, non-tactile acknowledgment. And this was the thing that got to Clem most of all: to find their relationship had deteriorated to the stage where they never so much as touched any more, where only in television soaps and cinematic fantasies were words of love ever spoken within his hearing; to find it had got to the stage where Yvonne would never so much as speak his name any more, to find that her attitude towards him (or so it seemed to him) might have been summed up by the simple question (unspoken, but none the less hurtful for that):

'What! You still here?'

And eventually, due to Yvonne's continuing coldness towards him, Clem Hardiker felt as if he were being almost physically restrained from touching her or from speaking to her any of those words of endearment that had previously been his wont. There was nothing in the world he wanted more than to touch her in the old way, to speak to her in the old way, to have those actions reciprocated by Yvonne herself as they had been so often in the past. But, over the years all hope of being allowed to do so became lost. And when hope took flight, other things took flight along with it.

So when, after a few years of his no longer being hopeful of re-accessing Yvonne's heart, he went back to drinking. That way, at least his lonely days was filled with voices, his lonely nights with slumber. And, after the passage of another dozen years or so, the problem of Clem Hardiker's enforced celibacy became merely academic: Clem Hardiker was now celibate *per se*. The discovery of Viagra might herald the prospect of a return to potency, but the Hardiker relationship, man with wife, was utterly beyond repair. Roslyn, the youngest, was eighteen years and two months old when Clem Hardiker left home for good. Not that he moved so very far away: he lived in Blackley still, in a two up, two down on Ruskin Street.

The Millennium. A heavy man exits the Museum pub after midnight, his clothes serviceable but not stylish, clean but unimpressive – an open necked white shirt, an anorak in a lovat shade, trousers of an indeterminate grey, Doc Martens on his feet. He hails a passing black cab without success (he fancies eating at the Akash in Market Place, Middleton).

'Dam-n-y e'spense!' he mutters under his breath. "S' Minn-ellium!'

Two further black cabs fail to stop. So the British Balti Tandoori Take-Away it will have to be – as, indeed, it is for him every Friday, Saturday, Sunday, high day or holiday, or any time our man has a yen for spicy eats and no access to transport.

'C'mo-o-n, yew Ble-e-ue-ue-s!' calls a two-some lurching good-naturedly from the doorway of the Ben Brierley on the opposite side of Moston Lane – Ted Airton and Sid Elslack, with whom the British Balti Tandoori Take Away-bound has shared a pint or three and an hour of his time earlier in the evening, during which the three of them have talked a good game of football in the lobby of the Ben Brierley: a better game by far than has been played at Maine Road for many a long year.

Clem Hardiker – for the British Balti Tandoori Take Away-bound is he – Clem Hardiker, formerly of Goodman Street and Westleigh Street, now of Ruskin Street, is 53 years of age, chronologically speaking, and 63 years of age in any visual sense. Clem Hardiker extends an underarm-delivered V-sign to Ted Airton and Sid Elslack, bringing that temporarily extended right arm back to the right-hand pocket of his anorak from which he sorts a Benson and Hedges cigarette packet and thence a cigarette, lighting it with the Colibri lighter he found on Clough Road at the corner of Westleigh Street when he was fourteen years of age. A couple of deep inhales power him to move onwards. Across Moston Lane we go to stand on the corner of Kenyon Lane, smoking, swaying, surveying the scene.

In the bus shelter on the opposite side of Moston Lane with St Dunstan's Lutyens-esque redbrick church for a backdrop someone is singing 'Candle In The Wind', and a girl begins to weep.

Clem Hardiker crushes the cigarette butt under one of his Doc Martens and checks the loose change in his trouser pocket.

What's it all about, eh? – Clem asks himself. Silly tart, crying over a kin song. Catch him doing owt like that! Hey, not more than once anyroad. Yeah, all right, but just the once, it was: that Saturday afternoon before Christmas in the house on Ruskin Street when he was waiting for the footy to come on ITV and listening to

Radio Two while he was waiting for it when all of a sudden that bastard Sedaka sneaked right up on him, singing 'The Hungry Years', catching him completely unawares.

'Co-o-me on, yew Ble-e-ue-ue-s!' calls Clem Hardiker to Ted Airton and Sid Elslack, lagging behind him now on the Ben Brierley side of Kenyon Lane – these four treasonous words passing his lips for the first time in his fifty-three years as a Manchester United fan – then, to himself *sotto voce*, as he reaches into the pocket of his anorak for his Benson and Hedges cigarettes and the Colibri lighter: 'Bollocks to it! Bollocks to the kin Minnellium!'

Charles Stiles (grandfather of Nobby Stiles, Manchester United and England), funeral director, corner of Alfred Street/Rochdale Road, 1968

175

35

Tall Storeys

i remember
i remember
them flats where i was born –
that litter-bugged grey landing
the stairwell's gaping yawn

> I remember
> One September,
> despatched to boarding school,
> Daddy lectured my headmaster there
> and made him look a fool.

i remember
i dismembered
our next-door neighbour's cat –
whirled its guts on skipping-rope
and hit me mates – KERPLAT

> I remember
> A November
> when snow fell mixed with rain.
> Daddy said: 'I say!' he said.
> 'Let's bagger orf to Spain!'

i remember
this distempered
rent-collector's dog –
it's cries lit up the lift-shaft
when i flushed it down our bog

I remember
That December,
when sleighs chimed at my door,
And I sauntered forth in apres-ski
to brighten Aviemore.

       i remember
       apprehension
       with me duffel bag of loot –
       one moonless night on our back stairs:
       this uniformed galoot

I remember
Commendation
as foremost civic martyr –
Receiving my due accolade:
The Order of the Garter.

       i reckon
       when i snuff it
       folk'll say – A pity
       there's still lame ducks like this'n
       in our cantilevered city

I envisage
When I pass away
panegyric editorials:
'Spirits such as his must fly
to their preordained Escorials!'

36

To The Most Reverend Pablo Puente,
Apostolic Nuncio to Great Britain

Your Excellency,

Ref: The Appointment of a new Archbishop of Westminster

As a Catholic layman formerly resident in the Diocese of Salford,
now retired to that of Menevia, and formerly resident too in the
Diocese of Sebastopolis, I wish to commend to Your Excellency
His Grace Archbishop Malchus Deepdale, DLitt, MA (erstwhile
Bishop of Sebastopolis) whose name has been mentioned in the
media of late as being amongst the most likely candidates to
succeed to the Archbishopric of Westminster.

Archbishop Deepdale is a holy man, a churchman of one mind
with His Holiness the Pope, a scholar of some distinction and with
the necessary maturity of years. His Grace is alert to the problems
of the age, and is mindful too of the poor in this country and
overseas. In short, were he appointed to Westminster, Malchus
Deepdale would be a teacher both by word and by example.

When he was Bishop of Sebastopolis in the early 1980s, he proved
himself intuitive in the extreme, introducing to the Diocese a
revolutionary sacramental programme with minimal use of the
consultative process. Bishop Deepdale was adaptable too, going
on to adjust the format of his sacramental programme on an annual
basis for the better part of a decade. Most importantly of all,
though, he proved to be decisive, driving his programme through
in the face of widespread opposition on all sides. And how
positive and optimistic was His Lordship's subsequent report to
the Holy See wherein he described the welcome accorded to his
programme as "unanimous".

Many were the prayers that were offered up on His Lordship's behalf until, eventually, he was translated to the Diocese of Tigia and Vagrauta.

Were he appointed to Westminster, His Grace would undoubtedly keep the Faith alive for the benefit of future generations, retreating (as is no doubt wise in this uncertain Nuclear Age) to a psychological Upper Room, as it were, until such time as society comes to its senses.

It is often said that we get the leaders we deserve and, with the new Millennium waiting to engulf us, we should perhaps hope and pray that, if it be God's Will, then His Lordship Malchus Deepdale, DLitt, MA, Archishop of Tigia and Vagrauta, will be chosen to lead us into it.
Yours,

Edmund Ealingham
Tyn Llyn, Prestatyn
North Wales
4 July 1999

37

To Edmund Ealingham

The Apostolic Nunciature presents its compliments and assures you that it has received your letter about the Archdiocese of Westminster. Your communication will be noted with thanks and taken into due consideration.

Apostolic Nunciature
Parkside
London.
7 July 1999

38

The Light of Day

"As we go to press news has just come in of the death in tragic circumstances of Jonty Wembury at his home in North Wales. A former Moonraker* and Blackley man, Jonty Wembury will be known to many in the town due to their business connections with him, or through his connection with charitable causes in Middleton and north Manchester.

"The family has said that, following a short delay, which they trust will be understandable in the circumstances, it is expected that the funeral service will take place at St Tudwal's Church, Beddnewyd, North Wales. Details to be announced. [See back page.]" *Hebers & Tonge Telegraph*, 14 March 2001.

John Theophilus Wembury (Jonty), who was 75 years of age at the time of his death, was born at Needham's Croft, off Rochdale Road, Blackley, which was accessed by means of a ginnel almost directly across from the front entrance of the former Harpurhey Baths.

'You'd go through the ginnel at the side of the Whispering Woman's toffee shop below Ray McGrath's bicycle and toy shop and two or three doors down from Kitty Dignan's confectioner's,' Jonty Wembury would say in his cups at Pike Fold Golf Club, 'those three establishments representing the totality of my leisure interests during my formative years, and our house – if you'd call it that: it was a dwelling really – our house was just there, over to your left. Daddy was a waste disposal operative, and the dustbin works (as we used to call it) was nobbut a cockstride away on Sidney Road at the bottom end of Russell Road, now Russet. But the Farmyard Hotel was even closer to home and the tap room of the Farmyard received far greater support from the old boy than the old girl ever got.'

But Jonty himself was destined for higher things, and, in 1938, he won a scholarship to Manchester Grammar School (a first for any pupil from Alfred Street School, Harpurhey). And it

* Moonraker: a Middletonian

181

was at Alfred Street too that Jonty had given a first intimation of that business acumen for which he would become famous in later life, showing a remarkable aptitude for the market place when he cornered the supply of conkers to his peers. Because, come the autumn term of his fifth year at Alfred Street, Jonty Wembury would have conkers on sale in the school yard at ten for a penny, having come across an infallible source of supply beneath a horse chestnut tree in a derelict Congregationalist churchyard above the district of Charlestown, south-west of Hebden Bridge – which remunerative location the boy Wembury thereafter made sure to access on an annual basis via the towpath of the Rochdale Canal.

Reaching the canal towpath at Slattocks, behind the Ship Inn, Jonty Wembury would walk the sixteen miles or so to Hebden Bridge and the same sixteen miles back each October half-term, staying overnight at his Grandma Widdop's house in the village of Colden. Of course, an additional bonus deriving from these annual conker-gathering sorties was that the young legs which were strengthened by this thirty-two mile round trip would greatly assist the young Jonty in affording personal protection to younger boys at the school at an individual cost of one halfpenny per annum – and in demonstrating too to those same younger boys the obvious desirability of accessing personal protection from him at the earliest possible opportunity.

'But,' Jonty would sigh in the locker room at Blackley Golf Club in later years, recalling the youthful business acumen that has on occasion been misrepresented in what Jonty always termed 'the gutter press' . . . 'But you may be certain that the High Master put a stop to any nonsense of that sort. Manchester Grammar School was a singularly civilised establishment in those days; still is. So I was constrained to take up photography instead; and from the age of eleven to the time I left school any subsequent business dealings were conducted (as was only right, I might add) in a manner that was altogether more genteel, and within a more select group of one's peers. Hah! Until even that enterprise had to be curtailed due to the groundsman's daughter being identified by her mother, who recognised the birthmark in one of the snapshots.'

Jonty Wembury's scholarship to Manchester Grammar School

was further distinguished by the fact that his mother, the former Matilda Widdop, poor and unschooled though she herself was, had the eminent good sense to recognise her son's scholarship opportunity for what it was. And from the first Tilly Wembury steadfastly encouraged the lad in his studies despite the quite debilitating domestic poverty in which her eight surviving children – four boys and four girls – were constrained to eke out a sub-consumptive existence on what little their father tipped up on a Friday night when the landlord of the Farmyard Hotel threw him out. Subsequently too, nothing would deter Tilly Wembury from her determination that Jonty, her third son, should avail himself to the full of the advantages to be had from the halls of academe. In this she was assisted by a memorable right hook which would have been impressive enough had it been delivered by Jackie Brown, the world-champion Manchester boxer then at the height of his fame, but which was even more impressive when delivered by a small fishwife of a woman to the jaw of her besottedly drunken spouse on his return from the Farmyard Hotel at 11.35 pm of a Friday night.

'I swear she's got,' Wenny (Weneceslas) Wembury, the spouse in question, would laughingly confess in the taproom of the Farmyard Hotel, 'more stamina than a steam hammer'. Even so, his cronies at the Farmyard were ever at a loss to understand how Wenny had had the ability, never mind the inclination, to father a set of twins upon her in the Jubilee year of His Majesty King George V.

And so, subsequently, and with his mother's unfailing support, Jonty Wembury went on to achieve high academic distinction at Manchester Grammar School and at the London School of Economics too, whence he emerged in the summer of 1948 with a double first to join Withers and Pratt's at its Philip's Park headquarters.

His father, Wenny, had died in Crumpsall Hospital in the last days of 1940, his demise coming about due to a fall down a ravine on the corporation tip adjacent to the dustbin works following a riotous session in the Old House at Home on the ICI path, where he had made light of the Luftwaffe's bombing of Manchester city centre. This, nevertheless, had so affrighted him on his way home later that night that it caused him to lose his footing at the top of Sidney Road and brought him to a slithering clinker-based halt sixty-five feet below the dustbin works near to Somerfield Road in the dip.

It is true to say that Jonty Wembury never had been as close to his father as he was to his mother, so it never did give him much cause for concern that, having been evacuated to Bright Street, Darwen, for the duration of the War, he missed his father's subsequent interment in Christ Church Cemetery, Harpurhey. But what was to be a source of constant regret to him, was that, when his mother died in the February of 1989, he would find himself prevented from returning home from Paris for her funeral due to the intricate and protracted nature of Withers and Pratt's reverse takeover negotiations with Rapishaw Gap, which were then entering their final phase.

But, as Jonty remarked to Mlle. Delphine Girondin, who was acting as his temporary secretary on that occasion: 'Asters Ad Astra is quite something, mam'selle. I really must pick up a tranche of its shares. I placed the order with them by telephone at nine o'clock on the Monday morning – nothing but the best, you understand, mam'selle – and a bouquet of flowers was duly delivered to Blackley Crematorium the very next day. I don't know about you, mam'selle, but it always seems to me that a bouquet is a much more cheerful alternative to a wreath.'

Mlle. Delphine Girondin knew better than to think otherwise, though Mlle. Girondin was certainly not a person who was above making an adverse comment should need arise. And as luck would have it, need *did* arise later in that same week during a gruelling all-night session in the negotiations when Mlle. Delphine Girondin slapped Mr J. T. Wembury's cheek soundly in the privacy of his penthouse suite which she had entered at two o'clock in the morning with papers Mr Wembury had omitted to sign. Precisely two minutes later Mlle. Girondin left Mr J. T. Wembury's suite with a blot on her copy book that would blight her career for the next twelve and a half years – until, in fact, the body of Mlle. Delphine Girondin would come to the surface of the River Seine adjacent to the *Palais de Justice* in the December of that year, the first of the new millennium. For on his homeward flight by British Airways out of Charles de Gaulle Airport Jonty Wembury had felt obliged to bring Mlle. Girondin's reference bang up-to-date by reporting that Mam'selle had proved to be 'reticent and uncooperative' and 'unamenable to directions given by the executive'.

It was in 1952, Her Majesty The Queen's Coronation Year, that Jonty Wembury married Jessie Albinson of Oakworth Street, Blackley – the youngest child of a family of ten – at St Bartholomew's Church, Bottomley Side, Blackley. And, until their retirement to Bednewyd in the autumn of 1991, the devoted couple were to remain worshippers at the Blackley church, Jonty acting as sidesman and churchwarden. Their first home together was on Polefield Road, Blackley.

'Nob Row, as I've heard it called on occasion,' Jonty would say in the locker room at North Manchester Golf Club, referring to the Wemburys' Blackley address and their brood of nine children (five girls and four boys) – 'and I *do* wonder why!'

And Jonty and Jessie (and, indeed, Janette, James, Jennifer, Jeremy, Joanna, John, Juliette, Julian, and Jasmine) remained in the house on Polefield Road until 1977 – Her Majesty the Queen's Silver Jubilee year – when they moved to a much larger house backing on to the woods on Meadow Road in Alkrington, Middleton, where they would remain until Jonty's retirement from work in 1991, Her Majesty The Queen's *'annus horribilis'*.

'Damned place was coming apart at the seams,' Jonty Wembury would reminisce about their Polefield Road house in the locker room of the Manchester Golf Course, 'with nine bread-snatchers roaming free range around it.'

And it was during these later years, from 1970 on, that Jonty Wembury was invited to become a trustee of the Moonraker Charities Trust (and latterly its Treasurer), in which capacity he became actively involved in both the administrative and the practical side of things.

The Moonraker Charities Trust had been set up during the

sixth decade of the nineteenth century in order to succour the poor and disadvantaged people of Middleton, Hebers and Tonge during the so-called Cotton Famine that threw many of the local cotton operatives out of work during the Union blockade of Confederate ports during the American Civil War, 1862-1865. Jonty Wembury was, of course, well-qualified to be a trustee of the Trust and, indeed, its Treasurer.

He had trained as an accountant and qualified as a chartered secretary and a certified accountant, gaining the distinction of winning the Abercrombie Abacus Prize for the highest marks awarded to a Mancunian student in the year 1950. And with distinctions such as these, Jonty was, naturally, a welcome addition to the board of trustees of the Moonraker Charities Trust – and to the board of directors at Withers and Pratt's, where he rapidly progressed upwards over the years.

In 1969, the year of Prince Charles' investiture as Prince of Wales, Jonty Wembury, at 40 years of age, became the youngest ever divisional director of Withers and Pratt's, and he now began to travel widely on company business, gaining personal directorships with Albion Metallurgies, Uniflex Intrusions and Aleutian Realities in addition to posts in an advisory capacity in Italy, Switzerland, Grand Cayman, and the Lesser Antilles with Ullapool Technologies and the Circumflex Management Group of companies. He had long since held high office in the Chartered Institute of Secretaries, and it was around this time too that Jonty Wembury initiated a truly innovative management policy at Withers and Pratt's (much lauded by his fellow directors) by means of which, 'to save time, money, and the blasted trouble of breaking in a new girl to my own personal requirements every time there's a new contract on the horizon' (as he was overheard to say in the locker room at Saddleworth Golf Club), Jonty would henceforth be able to employ his own personal secretary with Withers and Pratt's picking up the tab.

Accordingly, from 1967 to 1974, Miss Mirabelle St Henri filled this exacting role, working exclusively and quite selflessly on Jonty Wembury's behalf. Miss St Henri proved to be a thoroughgoing professional who readily understood what was required of her in the boardroom, the salon, and elsewhere. Indeed, she came to the job on the personal recommendation of no less a personage than T. Z. Wetherby, the Chairman of Rapishaw Gap. And during the seven years she was in Jonty Wembury's employ ('until St Streetwalker's thirteenth twenty-sixth birthday', as *Private Ear* glibly put it) Mirabelle St Henri accompanied Jonty Wembury to a score of spa towns and resorts within the UK, to six European capital cities, to Grand Cayman, Bermuda, and the Lesser Antilles. Then, in the same year that Mirabelle St Henri 'had to be put out to grass' (as Jonty Wembury laughingly described her departure in the locker room of Mere Golf Club), Jonty himself was placed in charge of the European division of Withers and Pratt's. It was in this capacity that he would become involved in its reverse takeover of the Rapishaw Gap Group in 1989.

But it was in this year also, following an anonymous tip-off, emanating from Biarritz (it was said) on Brinks Matt notepaper in (what was thought to be) a lady's handwriting, that difficulties began to beset Jonty Wembury's public life. And these difficulties would give rise to publicity of such an adverse nature that a shadow would be cast over the culmination of Jonty Wembury's public career and the well-deserved enjoyment of his retirement – which the kind would describe as 'premature', the sharp-tongued as 'overdue'. The aforementioned difficulties related to the Moonraker Charities Trust of which Jonty Wembury had been treasurer since 1972 and to a six figure sum that had been placed on deposit in a bank registered in Grand Cayman.

'It is, I suspect, purely fortuitous,' Mr Justice Hardraw Fitzhern declared whilst summing up at Manchester Crown Court on that February day in 1975 on which the matter of the Moonraker monies had received an airing quite as thorough as His Lordship's indictment of Tavistock Greenlee (whom His Lordship dubbed 'this ace newshound of the *Hebers and Tonge Telegraph*') that 'Mr Greenlee's efforts to daub the Wembury doorstep with dirt' had 'not led to a writ for libel being served upon him by the defendant'. Mr Greenlee had, the judge conceded, 'told nothing more and nothing less than the truth about this and other matters, though he had told it in such a manner as to give enhanced meaning to the word *innuendo*; and no doubt we might soon expect', said Mr Justice Hardraw Fitzhern too, 'to find Mr Greenlee's by-line blazoned across the front page of one of the more lurid tabloids that litter the news-stands nowadays'.

Furthermore, Mr Justice Hardraw Fitzhern made a point of reminding the jury that what Mr Greenlee had revealed about Mr Wembury's past misdemeanours could have absolutely no bearing on the case before them, there being such a thing as a statute of limitations in this country, 'thank God, or we could all be hauled over the coals any time a cheque book journalist chooses to highlight the peccadilloes of one's youth'. Why, His Lordship had supported Oldham Athletic when he was a lad! (*Laughter.*)

In any case, observed Mr Justice Hardraw Fitzhern, there were several factors that the jury would need to note concerning the Moonraker trusteeship and the money in question before they entered upon their deliberations.

First of all, the figure involved might well be a substantial amount, but large or small, it was, in essence, a single digit that had been omitted from a single column of figures – to wit, a number one. And, whilst this might tend to cast doubt upon Mr Wembury's actuarial abilities, it should not incline the jury to adjudge him a villain.

In the second place, the £100,000 in question had not been paid into one of Mr Wembury's personal bank or building society accounts. Had this been the case, of course, Mr Wembury would have been packing his bags to live at Her Majesty expense for a very considerable time indeed. However, the jury must remember that this had not been the case. The £100,000 in question had simply been transferred from one Moonraker Charities Trust account to another, this latter account being located in Grand Cayman because, as Mr Wembury had already pointed out, Grand Cayman afforded the Trust 'a more advantageous rate of interest'.

Thirdly, the jury might care to note that Mr Wembury was not the sole signatory to the Grand Cayman account; Mr Meredith Salter, Secretary to the Moonraker Charities Trust and a fellow member of the Watch Committee, was co-signatory to the account.

Furthermore, both men had freely volunteered this information in their depositions before the Court.

And finally, it was only Mr Hardraw Fitzhern's personal opinion, of course, but His Lordship felt it was 'sadly indicative of declining standards in modern society that the gutter press, masquerading as crusader, should be able to vilify with impunity the character of a man like Mr Wembury who had given so many years of selfless service to the community'.

There the matter rested, and Jonty Wembury walked away a free man, though he would never be asked to serve on the Middleton or Rochdale Bench, as a man of his obvious merits and achievements might have expected to be asked at his time of life. Nor would his name be put forward for consideration for honours that would have entailed a trip to Buckingham Palace in a morning suit. Another thing that happened was that Jonty Wembury's secretarial allowance was effectively cut in half – though, in fairness, it should be said that this was perhaps due to the business recession prevalent at the time rather than to any suggestion by the board of Withers and Pratt's regarding the probity of Jonty Wembury's actions on Grand Cayman. Jonty Wembury immediately cut his garments according to the cloth available to him.

The professional services of Mirabelle St Henri had come at a high price. But family – in the shape of Gwendoline, his son James' wife, age 21 in 1976 – was costed some 50% cheaper. And, from January, 1976 till March, 1978, Gwendoline Wembury accompanied Jonty Wembury as his personal secretary to a score of spa towns and resorts in the UK, to seven European capitals, and to Grand Cayman, Bermuda, and the Lesser Antilles. But as luck would have it, by the spring of 1978, Gwendoline was two months pregnant with her first child – a boy who would be the spit and image of his grandfather, though Jonty himself never could see the resemblance. Thus it was that Jonty's daughter, Jennifer, was called upon to volunteer her services from the summer of 1978.

Jenny Wembury was twenty years old in 1978. She was fair of feature, fairer of complexion, and quite the prettiest of Jonty and Jessie Wembury's five daughters.

189

'She is an absolute stunner,' Jonty Wembury once confided to friends in the locker room at Prestbury Golf Club. 'If she weren't my own daughter, I tell you, I'd give her . . .'

Jonty Wembury never did specify what he'd give his daughter, Jennifer, because at this point in the conversation his voice tailed off into a stirrup cup laugh. But the tenor of the conversation, coupled to the stirrup-cup laugh, led his companions to understand that it was not a wide berth that Jenny would have been given.

Jenny Wembury was pregnant by the Christmas of 1978, and a wedding was hurriedly arranged to her long-standing boyfriend, Milford Salter, the eldest son of Jonty Wembury's friend and business associate, Meredith Salter, co-signatory of the Cayman Islands account. The baby, a baby girl, Yvette, was born the following July.

Thereafter, after a bit of a blip in the late seventies, the 1980s – certainly from 1989 on – saw a succession of Jonty Wembury's personal secretaries emanating from Eastern Europe at a rate of pay that was even more economic. Olga, Katya, Karla, Nadya – these girls lasted two years each; Wanda lasted four.

'My word,' Jonty Wembury would say in jest in the locker room at St Andrews subsequent to his retirement, 'they were a Wanda-ful four years, simply Wanda-ful . . .'

Although he was involved in a busy and at times hectic business life, Jonty Wembury was at all times a devoted family man. Even when he was sometimes commuting across the Atlantic more regularly than David Frost he would always allow time for his wife Jessie and their nine children (Janette, James, Jenny, Jeremy, Joanna, John, Juliette, Julian, and Jasmine) and their (eventually, twenty) grandchildren – two of whom, Barry, 22, at the time of Jonty's death, and Jenny's daughter, Yvette, 20, were practically the mirror image of their grandfather, although Yvette had her mother's eyes and nose; Barry, his mother's hair and teeth.

And when Jonty retired at the age of 64 he was to take full advantage of the new quality time at his disposal to improve his golf, as well as seeing more of his family, including his twenty doting grandchildren. He also developed some skill as an artist and leaves behind him an extensive collection of fine works in his favourite medium, that of oils on canvas.

Immediately Jonty retired from work he and Jessie decided to leave behind their beloved Middleton and north Manchester and St Barnabas' Church, and to move to the village of Beddnewyd in Clywd, North Wales where Jonty was soon immersed in village life. It was not long before they found a new circle of friends centred around the parish church of St Tudwal where Jonty again served as sidesman and warden.

His son James delivered the eulogy at the funeral service at St Tudwal's church.

'Throughout his life,' said James Wembury, 'anybody who came into contact with Jonty Wembury would very soon be affected by him. The young schoolgirls, for example, who came knocking at his front door in Beddnewyd to see if Mr Wembury was coming out to play Hide and Seek (*muted, respectful laughter*), or those friends and acquaintances of his who enjoyed the numerous after dinner speeches for which he was renowned – and deservedly so.

'One thing is certain,' said James Wembury, 'things would soon be humming wherever Jonty Wembury was involved. Why, even at the age of 75 on the occasion of their Golden Wedding anniversary bash, Jonty Wembury was still able to have an audience of 90 invited guests buzzing for nearly an hour, something in which he was ably and willingly supported by the butt of many of his jokes over the past 50 years, his lifelong sweetheart, the ever-loving and faithful Jessie.'

At the funeral breakfast held after the service at St Tudwal's Church, a packed function room at The Druid's Arms listened to a further eulogy delivered by his son-in-law, Milford Salter, who described Jonty Wembury as 'a most unusual man who had risen high in the world of commerce, but who at all times remained constant in his love for his family and his ever-widening circle of friends and acquaintances. There would have been many in St Tudwal's Church today, in The Druid's Arms at this moment, and in the wider world abroad who would be deeply affected by Jonty

Wembury's passing, and they would all – every one of them – be very different persons for having known his like.'

The *Hebers & Tonge Telegraph* had sent a young reporter along to Beddnewyd. 'Never in the field of human mourning,' wrote Lambert Ealingham, aged 21, a Churchill buff with pushy parents and little else to recommend him, 'were so many tears shed for so long by so few.'

The story Lambert Ealingham wrote for the *Hebers & Tonge Telegraph* told of how Jonty Wembury's grand-daughter Yvette Wembury, aged 20, had found the body of her beloved grandfather with a knife-wound letting the light of day into his torsal cavity subsequent to his having disturbed an intruder.

The story Lambert Ealingham did *not* write for the *Hebers & Tonge Telegraph* (since he did not know of it) might have told also of the ripped bodice of Yvette Salter's dress and the word BASTARD! scrawled in lipstick on the dressing-table mirror in her bedroom. It might have gone on to mention too the two ladies of the family who quickly erased all traces of that word from the dressing-table mirror and, binding Yvette to silence until the police had completed their enquiries, returned downstairs immediately to effect a forced entry of the French windows, ensuring all the broken glass fell inwards.

The bread knife, wiped clean of Yvette Salter's fingerprints and Jonty Wembury's arterial blood was subsequently cast into Lake Bala early one Sunday morning nine months later and, coincidentally, on the same day that Mlle. Girondin's body was found in the River Seine.

PC Ivor Williams of the Gwynnyd Constabulary, Ivor the Police, driving home from his night shift in Wrexham to the village of Llandhu in his wife's Ford Fiesta Ka Collection saw no hand rise from beneath the waves to receive the bread knife, and the wind merely soughed and moaned. But it occurred to PC Ivor Williams that it was something other than a stone that the woman in the Paisley headscarf had thrown into the lake, and he decided to make a note of the registration number of the Mercedes E430 saloon she was driving.

192

The lads should experience little difficulty in retrieving whatever it was that had been discarded, provided they followed a line due east of the little parking bay beside the lake. PC Ivor Williams thought it most unlikely they would need to call upon the services of the Underwater Search Unit. But just to make sure of his bearings, he did a U-turn as soon as the woman in the headscarf had driven off and he parked his wife's Ford Ka Collection in the exact spot where the Mercedes E430 saloon had been parked. Heck! He had half a mind to retrieve whatever it was himself, except for the fact that it was a bit parky for skinny dipping that morning and it would be better for all concerned if he were able to call upon a reliable witness.

Fred Dawes TV and Radio, Rochdale Road, opposite Christ Church

Committee Men

I . . . ah . . . I . . . ah . . . I . . .
ah . . . sympathise . . .

                                 I . . . ah . . . I . . . ah . . . I . . .
                                 ah . . . ponder . . .

               I . . . ah . . . I . . . ah . . . I . . .
               ah . . . realise . . .

                                   I . . . ah . . . I . . . ah . . . I . . .
                                 ah . . . wonder . . .

I . . . ah . . . I . . . ah . . . I . . .
ah . . . crystalise . . .

                                   I . . . ah . . . I . . . ah . . . I . . .
                                 ah . . . *thunder*!

               I . . . ah . . . I . . . ah . . . I . . .
               ah . . . emphasise . . .

                                   I . . . ah . . . I . . . ah . . . I . . .
                                 ah . . . Con-dor!

I . . . ah . . . I . . . ah . . . I . . .
ah . . . organise . . .

               I . . . ah . . . I . . . ah . . . I . . .
               ah . . . *squander*?

I . . . ah . . . I . . . ah . . . I . . .
ah . . . finalise . . .

                                   I . . . ah . . . I . . . ah . . . I
                                 ah – ah-ahh—*ch-oooooh* . . .

To GMP Judicial Sertvices, Manchester

Sir,

Ref: Forced Entry – 7 Gargrave Avenue, Blackley

Please be advised that I fully intend to contact my MP, Graham Stringer, concerning your denial of the existence of "a formal appeals procedure in cases such as these", and with a view to insisting he should complain to the Home Secretary on the grounds that lack of an appeals procedure accessible to the general public may tend to enable – indeed, encourage – the Chief Constable of GMP and/or unsympathetic GMP Claims Investigators such as yourself to interpret the provisions of Section 17e of the Police and Criminal Evidence Act 1984 in an arbitrary manner (i.e. to the advantage of GMP and the detriment of potential claimants) when such an outcome may not necessarily have been the intention of Parliament when this legislation was enacted.

You will, of course, recall that subsequent to the sudden death of my father during my absence on holiday recently, emergency access was required to the above address where my disabled sister was in residence.

However, it remains my contention that the action taken by the police was excessive, resulting in repair costs amounting to £649.69, whereas my insurance company estimates that, had a locksmith been employed to effect access, costs might have been limited to approximately £80 in all. And the net result of this is that I have been unable to claim recompense for the expenditure under the household insurance policy, being constrained to pay for the repair work from my own resources.

Hope springs eternal, however, and I hereby reiterate my appeal to GMP for financial compensation in this matter.

Yours.

Eileen Ealingham (p/p Miss Frances Hareshaw)
Blackley, Manchester.
August 1995

* No financial compensation was forthcoming.

To Carpetbagger: the *Fiducial Times*

Sir,

Ref: The Trust from Hell

When my father died my disabled sister, aged 50, who had always lived at home with him, went to live with a local authority appointed family carer, her expenses being met by the DSS. My sister's needs are relatively simple: no Disneyworld visitor, she! But it very soon became clear that every last penny of DSS monies was being spent. Even so, the local authority refused to make the accounts available for inspection by an independent auditor.

But worse was to come.

My sister, I learned, was entitled to receive a residual pension from my father's former employer and, in order to protect her interests in the unsatisfactory financial situation in which she found herself, I appointed an accountant and instructed a solicitor recommended by Mencap to set up a discretionary Trust for her.

Officialdom now burst into life, levelling at me an accusation of fraud.

A tribunal has since found in favour of the Trust, but still the DSS persists in hounding me. Naturally, the fees of the professionals I retained have continued to mount, mopping up some 50% of the value of the Trust, though the matter remains unresolved. Moreover, the Inland Revenue has now saddled up to join in the chase.

My sister has since moved to sheltered accommodation where I feel she is no longer at risk financially and, personally, I am fed up to the back teeth with the Trust I set up. But is there any way out of the predicament in which I now find myself?

Assuming the Trust pays off the DSS, the Inland Revenue and every other creditor knocking at its door, would I then be able to walk away from it? Or have I created a monster that is destined to devour me?

Yours,

Eileen Ealingham
Blackley, Manchester
15 May 2000

Carpetbagger says: *What I can tell you is that Northern Cyprus is proving increasingly popular with tax tourists such as yourself.*

Booth's Furniture Store, formerly a billiard hall, corner Westbourne Grove/Rochdale Road. The World Famous Embassy Club (its entrance on Westboune Grove) shared the premises.

41

www.friendsreunited.com

Reminiscences from the Chalk Face

1947

From Tudor Avenue, facing the convent, you go through the gateway proclaiming 'Boys' and 'Girls', and turn right after a few yards into a dark passageway where Mrs Lingard and her helpers are hard at work in a room to your left, a room that exhales from its open door the smell of pure orange juice and milk at room temperature.

Bulldog (Alan Bulmer) is there before you, confiding in a whisper: 'There's no Father Christmas!'

(What does *he* know? Best keep an open mind as long as the presents keep turning up.)

Up the single step and turn right into Sister Mary Jerome's Reception Class where Sister keeps order with what subsequent study of Jimmy Cagney films and other films of that genre – Bogart, George Raft, Paul Muni – will reveal to be a blackjack, though Sister Mary Jerome's blackjack is made of wood and is applied to the palms of the hands, not the nape of the neck.

'No, you may *not* keep your gloves on, young man!'

One day, shortly before Christmas, with Sister out of the room on an errand somewhere, two five-year-old fun-guys, Terry Punchard and yourself do an osculatory lap of honour round the Reception Class, kissing every girl in the room. Puncher comes to no harm (the boy has obviously had his moments before); you, on the other hand, catch a cold and are off school for a week.

1949

Along that same unlighted infant school passageway, hacking your way through the smell of orange juice and manky milk with a make-believe machete. Up the single step, and right up to the top

198

of the passageway you go, where you take the second door to your right to access your class and Miss Bowland, your teacher in Top Infants with (in your left hand) a bunch of flowers your mother told you to deliver thereto.

You think so, boy? Not past Sister Mary Jerome, you don't! SNATCH!

'What a good little boy to bring flowers for our statue!'

Through Miss Tyrant's classroom you go, then turn left into Miss Bowland's room and get to your place, de-flowered. Miss Bowland's statue of the Virgin rebukes you not. Not so Miss Bowland, who icily lets rip.

Mary, Help of Christians, protect me before I even know your name!

1950

Peter Callis in Standard One in true *Dandy* and *Beano* fashion places a brass drawing-pin on teacher's chair, action-end up. (Were we all so completely stupid?) Time after time throughout that long summer afternoon Miss Elslack's tweed-skirted nether regions hover promisingly over that cruel instrument – and each time Miss Elslack's posterior hovers thus there is an expectant rush of air into forty pairs of boyish lungs, the owners of which – First Communicants to a man – are recently supposed to have accessed the age of reason.

This wonderful wind-up by Miss Elslack protects Peter Callis and the rest of us from the blistering gulag of punishment and shame that lies within the headmaster's – Old Hopalong's – fief.

1953

School trips are non-existent at St Joey's; so too are Art lessons, Science and PE. And it's just as well too. Because fripperies such as these are frowned upon by your dad (alumnus of the School of Hard Knocks, aka St Patrick's, Collyhurst). Yes, your dad knows exactly what serious schooling is all about.

So shame on Miss Rosemary Troup for organizing a boys'

choir to sing at Sunday Mass . . . for reading the story of Winnie the Pooh to you in class . . . for producing a magical playlet called *Puss in Boots* for your Christmas entertainment.

Neither is there a tuck shop as such, so everybody, individually – or so it seems – goes over the wall at playtime to stock up on ha'penny chews, banana splits, rainbow crystal, Chocstix, Black Jacks, liquorice sticks, and other confections at Mr Mac's toffee shop on James Street, where Mr Mac – bespectacled, flat cap aslant, ageless, incessantly chewing on the remnant of some anonymous sweetmeat – takes slabs of toffee, chocolate, treacle (in season), and breaks them with a toffee hammer.

Wealthier and more seasoned wall-hoppers, bored with this perennial performance, take themselves off to the Little Woman's toffee shop beyond the off-licence on the corner of Kemsley Street, where they splash out on Pendleton's Twicers.

1954

Fred Swellands, the new headteacher, introduces Music to the curriculum, an innovation that involves your class being taken out to the Prefabs (to Standard 8) on a Friday afternoon to listen to Swisher Swellands' record collection – all two of them, as I recall: 'Cool Water' by Frankie Laine, and the Oberkirchen Children's Choir, singing 'The Happy Wanderer'.

In Standard 4 too (Ozzy's class) an instrument of Inquisitional torture is in daily use – a school-book entitled *Train and Test* wherein Mathematical problems feature prominently, pummelling your young mind into insensitivity with questions involving: a) an escapee from Prestwich lunatic asylum who will insist on trying to run himself a bath without putting the plug in; b) a DIY dumb cluck who is inexplicably intent on weighing a brick and a half; and, c) a deluded time and motion expert who, being fully aware that 10 men can build a house in 6 months, sets a labour force of 1M to work and builds Langley Estate in a week.

Mid- to late-Fifties

Altar boys at St Joseph of Cupertino's church come under the supervision of Fr Richard Bellis, a newly-ordained priest who is landed with the job of arranging a rota of altar servers for four curates plus the parish priest on a daily and weekly basis. But the care Fr Bellis extends to the lads goes beyond this. Because on high days and holidays he undertakes also to transport hordes of you on day trips into the great, and previously unknown, outdoors. Thus, the world (specifically, that part of the world that is within striking distance of a day return rail or bus ticket) becomes our oyster.

Whalley Abbey . . . Pendle Hill . . . Edale in Derbyshire and Kinder Scout . . . Greenfield beyond Oldham and a mountain called Pots and Pans (where Line Bunratty entertains us by starting an avalanche of millstone grit) . . . but best of all, Hardcastle Crags near Hebden Bridge.

What we are most eager to sample at Hardcastle Crags are the stepping-stones said to bestride the stream there. Tony Dinch (sadly, recently deceased) is perhaps more eager than most. Running ahead of the main party, he finds the stepping-stones, loses his footing, and ensures that our first glimpse of Hardcastle Crags is a splash of quite epic proportions. Dinchy spends the rest of the day wrapped in Fr Bellis' raincoat while his clothes dry out.

I remember this was thought hilarious at the time, though I now believe it was something of a very different order indeed. For it occurs to me in retrospect that Dinchy is wrapped safely in Fr Bellis' raincoat still while the rest of us lads continue to bring up the rear.

Late-Fifties

The building that became, for a time, St Joseph's Social Club and, latterly, was flattened so as to build a small housing estate adjacent to David Lewis Recreation Ground (named, incidentally, for the founder of Lewis's department store) was originally a convent of the Frightful Companions of Jesus (as the nuns were disrespectfully known at street level). The convent housed a school for girls of primary school age who wore brown uniforms and who paid for the privilege of attending school. Sister Mary Jerome, the head of St Joseph of Cupertino's Infant School – who, I sometimes imagine, would have been capable of keeping a firm proprietorial grip on a Chicago speakeasy with Al Capone intent on muscling in – Sister Mary Jerome lived at the convent, as did Sister Mary Anselm, the head of St Joseph of Cupertino's Girls' School, who was a sweetie – quite possibly because her working day never brought her into contact with rapscallions such as myself.

The convent smelled of beeswax and candles and recently extinguished tapers when I was a kid, and when – on the feast of Corpus Christi in June (the Thursday after Trinity Sunday) – I and other altarboys would attend the procession held in the convent grounds in which an acolyte-escorted visit would be made to various grottoes dotted about the convent grounds.

The convent was beautiful, as I remember it – as indeed were the grounds, the procession, the Corpus Christi procession with special lanterns carried by the acolytes, and also the orange juice and iced fingers with which the nuns would regale us as soon as the crowds had dispersed.

1956

Two callow youths in the Upper IVs at Xaverian College, Manchester, both sporting yellow socks and Windsor-knotted royal blue and gold striped school ties – one of them, Vinny Kelton, sporting a slick quiff, the other (yours truly) with a short-back-and-sided Tony Curtis, raving about 'Heartbreak Hotel', which he's heard on Radio Luxemburg the previous night, and which the smidgeonly-smoother Vinny Kelton dismisses as 'this week's fad', whereupon Ashton Palais jiver Vinny confides:

'I took a girl home last night.'

You fain interest, though you're thinking to yourself:

'What the hell would he do with one at that late hour? She help his mam do the washing up? Wind the clock up? Put the cat out?'

Because never for a moment do you imagine that Vinny has taken the girl home to her own house – which is only right, suaver, and more opportunistic. Naturally, you have to wait till the end of the year before you get a girl of your own to take home.

She is two years older than you, works full-time at Woolworth's on Piccadilly, and would have eaten you alive had you not boned up on all-in wrestling in the meantime.

You still have a few things to learn, wrestling that is less than proactive amongst them.

1965

I think Mr McGruder, the former headmaster of St Athelstan's was a musician, says somebody on 'Teacher Memory'. Mr McGruder certainly was a musician. He was the son-in-law of a wonderful Albert Schweitzer of a gentleman complete with winged collar and white hair who used to play the organ at St Joseph of Cupertino's church and ran a private academy in a premises on Rochdale Road, Blackley, that is nowadays the offices of a taxi firm at the foot of Valentine Brow.

People used to refer to the old man as Professor Stanegate. He was the sort of person who never seemed to get any older – as if he had always been a man of mature years.

Mr McGruder was married to Professor Stanegate's daughter Primrose. They had two sons, Bernard and Anthony. Mr McGruder was the head of St Athelstan's immediately prior to the arrival of Basil Hanlith, when Mr McGruder left to become the head of All Vandals and Wreckers (as everybody calls the place with facetious accuracy) whence Mr Basil Hanlith arrived to take charge of St Athelstan's.

Mr McGruder was my first head when I left college; I liked him very much indeed. Within two years of my arriving at St Athelstan's in 1965 I had exactly what I wanted and needed in my class library and stock cupboard. Thereafter, I was destined to rub up against some real skinflint heads, the sort who would throw a fit if you needed so much as a pencil.

For me, the best things I know about Mr McGruder were

these: he was held in great respect by Miss Airton, who in those days took Junior One at St Athelstan's (which lady's judgment I invariably respected myself); and he was, as I understand it, a fan of Damon Runyon, as am I, guys 'n' dolls.

1965-66

The new building that St Athelstan's moved into in 1965, was one classroom short from the start. This meant that one class (not always the same class) had to be 'out' (wherever 'out' might be) for every lesson of every day of every week of the school year. So, Stan McGruder devised a rota whereby this might be achieved.

In the main it involved heavy dependence upon the Congregationalist hall at the top end of Smedley Lane and on the sporting facilities, such as they were, that were available at Smedley playing fields and Crumpsall Park. First thing Monday morning – when dinner moneys needed to be ready to hand – it involved taking two classes for Religion in the school hall, though what you can do religion-wise with sixty-five children unless you also have loaves and fish as visual aids is difficult to say. It was an achievement to get them to sit down and shut up – though why they should do either in such circumstances is also difficult to say.

My favourite 'out' time of the school year was cricket during the summer months, when, on a Friday afternoon, I'd take Miss Ann Thrope's boys and mine to Crumpsall Park. Never before that time or since have I played cricket at such a professional level. Usually I'd join in with the lads, but only as a fielder. And I did so on the grounds that an eleven-year-old boy who has not been 'in' has not played cricket. Generally speaking, with myself included as a fielder, all thirty-two of them would get an innings.

In retrospect, the only drawback to playing cricket in Crumpsall Park lay in being approached by a succession of cricketing internationals (Peter May and Typhoon Tyson of England fame amongst them) who were on temporary leave of absence from the Springfield wing of Crumpsall Hospital and were invariably available for selection.

1966

I have good reason to remember Jenny Ponden with her perfect white necklace of a smile, her clear complexion, her eminently-controllable and luxuriant mop of dark hair, her sparkling innocent eyes, aged 10, standing at the end of Smedley Lane with her back to the school railings – greeting me cheerfully as I returned, coatless, sopping-wet, hair-bedraggled, Italian-cut two-piece suit a wreck, winkle-pickers kaput, shirt collar and tie sodden, at the head of thirty-two drenched eleven-year-old boys who had walked, as had I, for two hundred yards from the Congregationalist hall at the top end of Smedley Lane in the pouring rain. Indeed, how could I forget Jenny's chirrupy cry:

'It doesn't look like you, sir!'

Gee, thanks, Jenny – but especially for a wonderful memory of a brilliant smile!

1966

Miss Airton's class circa 1966. What am I doing in there? I can't remember. Standing in for some reason – and immediately Miss Airton has left the room this seven-year-old boy (I'm tempted to call him Rodenberry, but the story's much more down to earth than *Star Trek*), this seven-year-old called Rodenberry (or something) says:

'Psst! Wanna map o' the world, sir?'

And myself not demurring, Rodenberry whips said Mappa Mundi off in ten seconds flat – five continents, seven seas: the lot! Hey, presto! A 2HB-pencilling prodigy!

Come on, own up if you were that cartographical First Communicant! I thought you were a genius then, and I do still – and I couldn't get out of that classroom fast enough before my own vast inadequacy should be revealed.

Tell us who you are, and tell us you've been drawing something better than the dole ever since.

1965-67

1965 sees four teachers on the level above the foyer in the new building. Going clockwise from the school entrance they are yours truly (Junior 3), Miss June Huntley (Junior Two), Miss Marjorie Airton (Junior One), and Miss Ann Thrope, the deputy head (Junior 4). Miss Sue Hennessey has a class (another Junior 3, I think it was) across the playground in the old school.

'Fit to stable horses a hundred years ago,' is the description of the old school with which Stan McGruder regales any visitor with clout. 'Fit for schoolchildren today.'

A giant pin-board in Stan's office gives precise details of the hordes of children currently on roll. The vividly-coloured plastic numerals Stan uses for this enumerative task would have mesmerised a pre-cured Bartimaeus. But for the academic year 1966 to 1967 Stan hits on a new way of impressing the actuality of the school's demographics on the visiting world: two classes are to be housed permanently in the school hall. Eddie Ealingham, a guitar-strumming thespian, has one of them; and I have the other – bang up against a floor-to-ceiling window wall.

On one particularly hot July day, with a westering sun blazing through the window wall at three o'clock in the afternoon, we are so hot that . . . Michael Kimmins has stopped talking for the first time in nine months . . . Duncan Humesett is a pool of sweat on the floor (and the lad a non-swimmer still!) . . . and Hermione Frost is minded to change her name to Heavy-Dew. (It's true that Andrea Mickleton has slammed shut in disgust her Everyman copy of *The Prince*, but this has nothing whatsoever to do with the ambient temperature prevailing in the school hall and everything to do with Niccolo Machiavelli's not being the writer Enid Blyton is.) I, on the other hand, merely remove my jacket the better to regulate my body thermostat, but am copped immediately I drape it across the back of my chair.

Miss Ann Thrope, walking across the hall towards the infant block, expresses shrill surprise: 'Mr *Harney*! Your *jacket*!'

Obviously, I look ridiculous wearing the top hat without it.

1967

Was it Miss Airton's retirement party, or could it have been some sort of a get-well celebration? Again, I can't remember. But, whatever it was, I found it impressive – as, indeed, I invariably found the lady herself.

Miss Airton had taken some sick leave following the death of a close relative whom she had tended for many years. On her return to school (or, indeed, on the occasion when she was retiring) the Acting Chief Education Officer (I seem to recall his name was Halterburn) called in to school to extend his good wishes to her.

I still find this amazing, though it really was very much in keeping with the LEA's persona in those days – caring, committed, and truly compassionate. I used to say to my wife that I would rather be working where I was than on holiday in any other LEA in the country.

Hey, the new boys soon put a stop to such silliness mid-seventies on. You don't think things can change that much? You checked up on new Labour recently? But never mind all that. Because this is about something real – or, rather, someone: Miss Marjorie Airton, God bless her!

1972

What a great headteacher was Fred Swellands at St Joseph's. I never had the pleasure of working for him, but I know from personal experience he was a sports fanatic who pulled out all the stops for St Joseph's teams.

One time at the Catholic Sports at Melland Playing Field, Gorton, I'd done the best I could for St Athelstan's by complaining that the Assumption, Langley, had an unfair advantage when it came to the high jump event, though I was overruled by a judge with right on his side and no sense of humour. Still you've got to try; and Fred Swellands certainly did.

The 100 yards race was under starter's orders when Fred Swellands pleaded with the starter to hang on a minute on the grounds that his lad was 'queuing up for an ice cream'.

Unbelievably, the starter did just that, whereupon the St Joey's lad creamed it, having had the foresight to leave Fred Swellands holding his cornet.

1975

The late, lamented Chadderton (Chad Ireton), R.I.P., wins 'The Saddleback', the cross country race wearing a duffel coat. The same guy, is on the Smedley Fields one afternoon in all the insignificance of his five feet nothing height plus strabismus, when that basilisk of a Cockney PE master with the Irish surname from All Vandals and Wreckers (McKlondike, is it?) strides right up to him in the *oberleutenant* manner that is his wont, and stands towering above Chad like the CIS office block, whilst bellowing at some miscreant in the middle distance.

Chadderton backs off not one inch. He tilts his head backwards, looks this hulk in the nostrils at a distance of two feet six, and enquires:

'Hey, mis-*toh*, you an Australian?'

1979

School report time, and Carl Cronkley, who's more famous for shinning up a drainpipe on to the school roof than for academic effort and achievement, gets a consistent E minus on the report he's sent home with.

Next day the report is back in school with parents' comments duly noted in the space provided: 'Desert Orchid, 2.30 Catterick – WON'.

Surely the little scamper marks surrounding the announcement merit an A+ for artistic endeavour.

2002

Publication of Terry Eagleton's book *The Gatekeeper* finds myself and Vinny Kelton at Waterstone's on Deansgate one evening recently where Professor Eagleton, formerly Cantab. and Oxon., and now Man U(ni), treats us and a roomful of respectful

Mancunians to a reading from his book, and afterwards to autographed copies thereof, our own amongst them.

Naturally, the boy Kelton reminds Professor Eagleton of the time (1961, it was) when he had visited our old alma mater with a debating team from De La Salle College, Pendleton. The visit had taken place at the behest of L. W. Dever, Xaverian's historian of hallowed memory, who is destined to be so shallowly remembered in *Little Wilson and Big God*, the first part of what Anthony Burgess describes as his *Confessions*.

It had been the boy Kelton who took Terry Eagleton on in debate on the occasion of his visit to the school, and, as Vinny confesses at Waterstone's that night:

'It was a bit like throwing your coat down for a kick about in the school yard only to find the other side's fielding George Best.'

Terry Eagleton well remembers playing away that night, though he doesn't rub it in, failing to oblige me with the requested inscription: 'Wiped the floor with Kelton' in my copy of his book.

Still, old habits die hard, and Vinny and I soon revert to type – corny jokesters of the First Remove.

Approaching the meeting room on Waterstone's third floor, the various ablutionary facilities are duly noted – Ladies, Gents, and so on.

'What's that other door, there, you reckon?' says Demosthenes' doppelganger, Kelton. 'I don't suppose it's the Philosopher's Stone by any chance?'

Nugent's, painters and decorators, corner of
Mary Street/Rochdale Road, 1968

42

www.friendsreunited.com

Incommunicado –
an Ode to Non-Responders on the Internet

Who are these non-responders whose names appear on screen?
Why ever did they put them there? For reasons vague, unseen –
Though not obscene like mine opine: I think it's pretty chronic
To fly a flag for all to see with no biog upon it.
Friendsreunited, their proud boast – Ha! Silence gives the lie!
If friendship (theirs) were ever such, then porcine litters fly.
Fie! leave them to primeval sloth – I say to them: 'Get netted!
Had'st they *cojones* to respond, think'st they we'd have them vetted?
And so a pox on all such mutes, for right guys answer back–
Leave those who don't to voyeur's lens, Colombo's crumpled mac.
Forsooth, I drop them like a stone, their fall from grace observéd,
Ere two lines grant more than their worth – a sonnet undeservéd!

43

To *Mailbag*, the *Hebers & Tonge Telegraph*

Sir,

I was surprised to read a report in this newspaper recently to the effect that Her Majesty the Queen thinks the city of Manchester is "not such a nice place".

During the mid-1960s I once glimpsed the Royal limo as it whisked Her Majesty and the Duke of Edinburgh along Hulme Hall Lane, Miles Platting, towards the gates of what was at that time the thriving engineering firm of Withers and Pratt's.

Now, I have always maintained that as the Royal party swept past that spot adjacent to the Tripe Colony where I stood with my bedraggled streamer and a Mancunian crowd of similar ilk, Her Majesty the Queen – in quick response to some merry quip that had issued from the lips of the Duke – turned to her consort and declared:

'Yes, dear, and one could love a *pied-à-terre* up Corelli Street!'

Sadly, I now find I stand corrected, and I can only surmise that the word I took to be 'love' was in fact 'shove'.

Obviously, my lip reading skills leave much to be desired. Nevertheless, I am not prepared to accept that they were so wide of the mark as to lead me to substitute the phrase 'up Corelli Street' for a more humdrum phrase, anatomical or otherwise.

Yours,

Chrys McClintock
Rhodes Village, Middleton.
3 November 1999

44

Without Patrick Swayze Strutting His Stuff

'Well, seeing as you mention it, Benny, I do recall thinking to myself at the time: "Hullo, hullo, hullo, there would certainly appear to be something very fishy indeed about this, Don"' said Sergeant Don Jarvis, turning from the urinal and zipping himself up as the sprinkler system sprang into action. 'Not that either one of them was in any way out of place, you understand, be it in each other's company, or in that particular location at that hour of the morning – Ricky 'Stop-Me-And-Buy-One' Ballistic of this parish and Louise . . .'

'Del Monte,' said Custody Sergeant Benny Wessenden to the white tiled wall above the urinal at which he stood, shaking, prior to reeling in, or so it would seem, a line that had been used to catch marlin.

'*For God's sake, Benny*' – thought Don Jarvis, approaching the wash basins to make his ablutions – '*I've seen Les Hiddins, the Bush Tucker Man, extricate a Land Rover from Cape York in The Wet with less palaver.*'

'Oh, Del Monte is, er, was it this week?' he said aloud, pressing the hot tap and reaching for the liquid soap. 'Knew it was some household product or other, though Paxo would have been more honest in view of her game.'

'Why? Where's honesty come into it?' Benny Wessenden joined Don Jarvis at the wash basins as a thunderous fart from the interior of the nearest of the three cubicles broke in on their conversation, whereupon Sergeant Benny Wessenden, turning, addressed himself to the cubicle's unseen, yet anally vocal, occupant. 'You should've left that Chicken Vindaloo alone like I told you to, Hulbertson, old chum.'

PC Paul Hulbertson (who was not Sergeant Benny Wessenden's old chum, as it happened, but rather his subordinate), unseen still, responded with an instruction for Benny Wessenden to do something physically impossible, requiring as it would do, more ability than a contortionist could muster and the involvement of no consenting partner. PC Hulbertson had obviously mistaken the voice that had addressed him.

'Oh, not your old Sergeant, I don't think, Hulbertson, old chum,' said Benny Wessenden. 'No, no, no, no, no. Oh, dear me, no. It occurs to me, Hulbertson, old chum, that your old sergeant, would have you up on a charge before he'd consider an option such as that.'

'Sarge,' said P C Paul Hulbertson acquiescently, unseen still, and ripping another one off with what might be taken to be a tad more discretion.

'Yes, Don,' said Benny Wessenden, resettling, or so it seemed, a furled golf umbrella within his undergarments. 'As I was saying before I was so rudely interrupted: Miss Louise 'Buy-Two-And-Be-One-Jump-Ahead' Del Monte, slag of this parish.'

'For pity's sake, Benny.' Don Jarvis reaching for the roller towel, began to dry his hands. *'Fold the bugger in half and have done with it.'*

'The very gal,' said Don Jarvis.'

'But at the risk of repeating myself, Don . . .' Benny Wessenden now reached in turn for the roller towel. 'At the risk of repeating myself, what exactly was it that put you on to them in the first place?'

'Ah, Benny!' Don Jarvis tapped the side of his nose with the full length of his right index finger, treating Benny Wessenden to a knowing look. 'That's where all your Sedgley Park training comes into it's own, don't-cha think?' He opened the door now, allowing Benny Wessenden to pass through on to the main corridor that led down to the staff canteen.

As an afterthought Benny Wessenden shifted the position of a Winchester 73 within his blue serge uniform trousers. Don Jarvis – only that week returned from a five year stint in the Longsight and Moss Side districts of Manchester – Don Jarvis ignored this, warming to his theme as he and Benny proceeded along the corridor in the direction of Plant Hill Road and their respective breakfasts.

'The designer clothes were fine – though they were, of course, infinitely finer than anything you or I could afford. But everything

214

seemed to be above board in that respect is what I mean, Benny. The Jimmy Choo shoes, the Versace coat and gown for Madame; milord's biscuit-coloured jacket by Aquascutum with the Don Johnson-style turned-back cuffs, the Gucci shoes, the gold wristwatches . . .'

'Baume et Mercier for her, Cartier for him. I seen, I saw, Korky checking 'em in when I came on. And the rest of the stuff. The St Christopher medal (didn't do him much good, did it?), hefty diamond-cut curb chain, full sovereign ring – all three of them in 22 carat gold, for Mon-sewer; eh? And for Mam'selle . . .'

'Er, Madame, Korky tells me.'

'For *Madame*,' said Benny, 'a set of half carat diamond earrings, 22 carat diamond pavé bangle, and the rings – a good half dozen of 'em, as I recall, Don. Lemme see now: sapphire, ruby, emerald, amethyst . . . no, aquamarine, it was, wasn't it? Birthstone maybe. And a full one carat solitaire diamond engagement ring . . .'

'*Plus* the wedding ring, don't forget. A brooch too, wasn't there? A pinky thing.'

'A *pinky* thing?' Benny Wessenden feigned Petronian distaste. 'You utter vulgarian, Jarvis? I take it you mean, Madame's brooch in coral and pearl?'

'Ooh, coral and pearl, eh? Nice . . . And, know what, Benny? Not one piece of that jewellery seemed in any way out-of-the-ordinary, considering the two that was, the two that were wearing it: our Ricky, Ricky Ballistic, the driver, and Madame Louise, the passenger, in Mon-sewer Ricky Ballistic's Porsche 911 Carrera Cabriolet . . .'

'The red one?'

'Blue. Must've swapped it.'

'Kin red one was only last year's reg.'

'Yeah, but our Ricky always was very particular, wasn't he, Benny? Fussy even. Mind you, he wasn't that fussy he was concerned about a bit of dandruff on his jacket lapels.'

'Dandruff?'

'I employ a metaphor, my son, what with snow being unseasonal this time o' year. No doubt forensic will tell us more.'

'Well, go to the top of the class, Sherlock,' said Custody Sergeant Benny Wessenden as they reached the door of the staff canteen. 'So that's all you had to go on, was it, Don?'

'Well, no. Not quite all,' said Sergeant Don Jarvis, pushing through the door of the staff canteen and holding it back for Benny Wessenden to walk through ahead of him.

'Ricky Ballistic was' – wrote Tavistock Greenlee six months later in the New Year Bank Holiday weekend edition of the *Argolis* supplement to the *Sunday Thames* – 'a man as we are men. He shared our foibles, our virtues and our fears. Oh, we fooled ourselves into thinking – or more precisely, we allowed ourselves to be fooled by the literate guardians of our consciousness into thinking that Ricky Ballistic's weaknesses were greater than our own, his appetites all-consuming. But it simply was not true. Ricky Ballistic was as we are: he was a man as we are men. True, Ricky Ballistic was a man, writ large.. But the only meaningful difference between Ricky Ballistic and lesser mortals was this: Ricky Ballistic lacked certain blessings that the commonality of men is fortunate to enjoy, though this is not to say that the aforementioned commonality of men would necessarily regard the lack of such things as blessings. For the truth of the matter is that for the better part of his adult life (and many would say the worse) Ricky Ballistic was unrestricted by certain God-given restraints upon his appetites – restraints that tend to be exercised of necessity upon the appetites of that aforementioned commonality of men – restraints which are consequent upon a lack of sufficient finance in the first place, upon a degree of personal indolence in the second, and, ultimately, upon the need to account for our time, movements and whereabouts to our loved ones.

'Ricky Ballistic had money and to spare,' said Tavistock Greenlee. 'Ricky Ballistic had more money than any man could reasonably want or ever need – money to impress the club owners, the restaurateurs, the *maitres d* throughout the conurbation – and, indeed, the country; money to treat (and on a lavish scale) those whom money will ever befriend; money sufficient to pay for every one of his personal indulgences and mistakes, bar one.

'Ricky Ballistic had fame too,' said Tavistock Greenlee in the New Year Bank Holiday weekend edition of the *Argolis* supplement to the *Sunday Thames*. 'Therefore Ricky Ballistic had no need to sell himself since others fell over themselves to sell themselves to him. The national names – those born to shop and spend (themselves, their friends and family, anybody close to them, plus anything publicist Mickey Clapperbridge or the libel lawyers can contrive to secure for them); the cock-a-hoop sports personalities whose conception of 'scoring' coincides closely with its definition in the tabloid press, having nothing whatsoever to do with the scoreage of goals for or against; the celebrities (from the A list to the D); the people who constantly hog the headlines; the glitterati amongst us – the *coruscandi* (as Tavistock Greenlee put it, thereby introducing those of his readers who were still with him at this point to a word of his own design); the fly-by-nights; the detritus of failed marriage to royalty; the legends of stage and sceen; those who are famous for being famous . . . and the women. They all made their own running.

'Ricky Ballistic had time on his hands too,' said Tavistock Greenlee in the New Year Bank Holiday weekend edition of the *Argolis* supplement to the *Sunday Thames*. 'Plus he had the latitude and the inclination to use that time exactly as it pleased Ricky Ballistic to use it. The whole wide world was Ricky Ballistic's playground and all the goods within it were Ricky Ballistic's for the taking.'

In the early hours of the Sunday morning when Sergeant Don Jarvis's path crossed his own, Ricky Ballistic was in his native north Manchester, checking up on certain of his operations there. But Ricky Ballistic might just as easily have been anywhere else in the world where tides of money are known to ebb and flow, though not necessarily at street level as did his operations in north Manchester – St Peter Port in Guernsey; Douglas in the Isle of Man; Stockholm; Budapest; Moscow; Singapore; Los Angeles; New York, Zurich. And why ever not? Why not, indeed? Just as long as you have fame and fortune and time on your hands and the determination to employ these things to their fullest extent, and your name is Ricky Ballistic.

And, subsequent to the widespread public interest which would appear to have been engendered by Ricky Ballistic's recent demise in that same locality – engendered, that is to say, by the public's long-standing vicarious involvement in Ricky Ballistic's life-style when combined and contrasted, overnight, as it were, with that same public's horrified delight in the suddeness and finality of Ricky Ballistic's despatch from this mortal coil (sentiments which, it is only fair to say, have been nurtured most assiduously by certain sections of the popular press) . . . Yes, subsequent to this it might well be that, once the dust has settled, an investigative journalist of a more serious frame of mind (the aforementioned Tavistock Greenlee, for example, late of the *Hebers & Tonge Telegraph*, the *Daily Mess*, and more recently columnist in residence for the *Et in Arcadia Ego* feature in the *Argolis* weekend supplement of the *Sunday Thames*) . . . Yes, it is only to be expected that such a journalist might wish to delve just a little more deeply into the nature of the beast that was Ricky Ballistic. (Incidentally, this would perhaps be a touch ironic in that Tavistock Greenlee would thus, simultaneously, profit from the tabloids' dirty work whilst purporting to prove himself their superior.)

And, as his starting point, the aforementioned Tavistock Greenlee might take it into his head to go right back to the beginning, so to speak, by seeking to consult the records held at Manchester Register Office on Deansgate, and the baptismal register at the parish church of St Joseph of Cupertino, situate in the postal district of Blackley, in the City of Manchester, in the Roman Catholic Diocese of Salford, in the Province of Liverpool, in the Archdiocese of England and Wales. And, more specifically – and if Mr Greenlee is, indeed, the journalist we take him to be – he might choose to concentrate his attention on those pages of the baptismal register which record the administration of the sacrament during the early part of January in the Year of Our Lord, 1970.

A merely casual enquirer would be disappointed at the outset. For there exists no baptismal record under the name Ballistic, because Ballistic is a nickname, of course. But Blackley people

218

whose memories range back through the last half century on the streets of north Manchester will recall Ricky Balanciaga, the youngest of the three Balanciaga brothers, first acquiring the nickname Ballistic subsequent to a summer's evening in 1988 when Ricky Balanciaga was eighteen years old and bloodied a Carmody in a fist fight.

This event – which occurred on a bombsite on Factory Lane adjacent to Barnes Green Social Club and the Corporation yard (that is, on the site of the erstwhile Empire Cinema) – this event would necessitate twenty-two successive and individual street fights, in every one of which Ricky Balanciaga (hence, and henceforth, Ballistic) was victorious against twenty-two male representatives of the Bimberg, Booth, McClelland, McKay, Roscoe, Gallacher, Farrell, Harper, Bardsley, Tamburro, Estall, Shepherd, Livesey, Kilburn and Lebrun families, who were all interrelated and who all considered themselves to have been bloodied when the Carmody was bloodied – which, of course, they all eventually were, within one calendar month of the August Bank Holiday Monday of that year, by Ricky Balanciaga's head (the Manchester Kiss that broke Bobby Bimberg's nose), and subsequently by his teeth, elbows, shoulders, fists, knees, feet – and in one instance, by his posterior: specifically, Edgar Lebrun, when in a state of near exhaustion Ricky Ballistic sat upon his opponent's head precipitously, and 'from a dizzy height' – as Ricky Ballistic so described it – ' of three foot kin six!'

Ricky Ballistic, who was to win for himself such street acclaim and notoriety, was baptised in the church of St Joseph of Cupertino following his delivery in the maternity wing of Crumpsall Hospital at four minutes past ten on a Monday night that was reputed to be the coldest November night for eleven years, the details of his baptism being recorded under the family name, Balanciaga.

Just six people witnessed the christening of the youngest Balanciaga on that Sunday afternoon in early January: his father, Martin, who seemed to be somewhat preoccupied throughout the ceremony; Herbert Ellison, the sacristan at St Joseph's, who had volunteered to be the baby's godfather; Judith Joyce, the baby's maternal aunt and godmother; his older brothers, Frank and Vinny; and Fr Declan Ward, who conducted the ceremony in his habitually quasi-belligerent fashion.

Fr Ward had been a popular priest in his prime, but Fr Ward's prime was long since past. At the time of Ricky Balanciaga's christening Fr Ward was in his seventy-seventh year and struggling to hold the parish together following the sudden demise of two parish priests within two years, Fr F. X. Elrick and Fr Bernard Grindslow, who had been Fr Elrick's replacement. Fr Ward was well-loved by the parishioners of St Joseph's, but he was loved with the kind of love that respects a man for what he has once been, not for what he has become. And in his not infrequent moments of perspicacity this thought and thoughts akin to it troubled Fr Ward greatly. It was very good of everybody, it was most loyal – it was, to be perfectly honest about it, no more than Fr Ward's due. But it was a patronising sort of love at best, the kind of love that humours you – the kind of love that, smilingly, is prepared to clear up after you when you go and make a mess of things once again just as everybody fully expected you were going to do in the first place.

Mary, Help of Christians – Fr Ward prayed silently as he approached the baptismal font with Herbert Ellison and the Balanciaga family – *help me in my hour of need.*

Forgetfulness was the bane of Fr Ward's old age, the penultimate cross he had to bear. (Fr Ward's final cross would be the massive stroke he would suffer during the excitement of the preparations for the parish procession the following June. Thanks to the care he received in the Alexian Brothers' Home, Moston, he lingered through the remainder of that summer but passed away quietly on the 24 September, the feast of Our Lady of Walsingham.) And forgetfulness was the cross Fr Ward found hardest to bear – it was a failing he was ashamed of and which he tried to cover up with grumpiness and bluster. Even so, he knew he was fighting a losing battle. No amount of bluster could cover up his omission – until Herbert Ellison took his courage in both hands and entered the sanctuary to remind him ('Steady on, now,

Father. You're not riding that AJS Porcupine of yours down Factory Brow with the wind behind you like you used to do!') – no, no amount of bluster could cover up his omission of the Sanctus from the Mass of the Holy Innocents on the 28 December last.

Thank God – thought Fr Ward – *thank God for Herbert Ellison and others like him!*

Throughout the christening of the boy, Richard Edward Balanciaga, Fr Ward had been plagued by a nagging feeling that the ceremony was somehow incomplete. And his grumpiness showed itself all the more whilst he fretted about it.

'Eh? Eh? *Ricardus Eduardus, Ego te baptizo in nomine Patris et Filii et Spiritus Sancti.*' (The Latin '*z*' being an approximation of '*dzeta*', the sixth letter of the Greek alphabet, Fr Ward pronounced the word *bap-tidzo*.)

Yes – yes, that was it! there was to be no churching of the mother, a ceremony current in that time and place. *Where was the blithering woman?* Fr Ward very nearly spoke the thought aloud until he glanced uncertainly at Herbert Ellison, and something, something in the expression on Herbert Ellison's face prevented him from doing so. *Eh? Eh? . . . Ah!* Slowly, vaguely – very slowly and very vaguely – Fr Ward remembered that he had himself said the Requiem Mass for Maria Balanciaga only ten days before and, accompanied by Charlie Stiles, the funeral director (father of Nobby Stiles, the Manchester United football player and England international), had escorted her mortal remains to their final resting-place at St Joseph's Cemetery, Moston.

Oh, God! God! Was that the same day he had omitted . . . No, no, not the day of the Consecration lapse. No, that was the day he very nearly omitted the Creed, that is, until Herbert Ellison's tactful fit of coughing had reminded him of it.

Of course, had Tavistock Greenlee planned any such investigation of the origins of Ricky Balanciaga, aka Ricky Ballistic, he would, have been disappointed at a more seminal stage – if, for instance, he had been unfortunate enough to seek access to the baptismal register and been met by Canon Thomas Pavor, who was the parish priest of St Joseph's parish in April, 2002, at the time when Ricky Ballistic (*né* Balanciaga) met his fate.

The Very Reverend Canon Thomas Pavor, MA, STL, RD would almost certainly have refused Tavistock Greenlee access to the baptismal register for the year in question – or for any other year, if it came to that. Never a man to suffer fools gladly, no gloss had been added to Canon Pavor's good humour by the twin facts that he had spent more than thirty years as parish priest in the ecclesiastical backwater of St Joseph's, and – despite his obvious erudition and talents – had been overlooked for any preferment whatsoever until the winter of 1983/4, when he had been elevated to the rank of honorary canon and Rural Dean. This was in the hiatus between the retirement of Bishop Thomas Holland in June, 1983 ('Sailor Sam', as Canon Pavor had been indiscreet enough to refer to His Lordship in the presence of Fr Philip Newfield, a former curate at St Joseph's) and the appointment of Bishop Patrick Altham Kelly to the bishopric of Salford in April, 1984.

Canon Pavor kept a house dog, a Kerry Blue called Tadgh. It was the loyalest beast known to man, a comfort by the fire on a winter's night when the Canon sipped his Glenmorangie neat and chased it down with the steaming Bourneville cocoa that Mrs Keating, his housekeeper, provided prior to retiring for the night. It would be a hardy cleric or parishioner who would think of disturbing the Canon at such a time, for the dog was a veritable scourge to the rest of human kind. Countless altarboys could attest to the strength of its jaws, and Christopher Stanegate, aged 7, swore the dog had sought to de-sex him when, subsequent to a copious intake of orange cordial on his birthday, he had emerged from the conveniences adjacent to the sacristy in the process of adjusting his dress.

On one occasion, whilst the presbytery was undergoing redecoration, the dog had ripped the nose from the face of a workman who had claimed to have knowledge of the ways of animals. Moreover, the Canon himself was known to take a perverse delight of a summer's evening in letting the dog roam at will in the disused allotments across the road from the presbytery where it would flush out impecunious, ergo *al fresco*, lovers from the cover afforded them by the Manchester poplar trees and

222

clumps of tussocky rye grass which were the only crops the allotments ever produced. Certainly, Canon Pavor would have been in no way reluctant to sic the dog on an over-paid and over-confident heathen like Tavistock Greenlee, quality newspaperman or no.

But in fact, barring the clergy attached to St Joseph's parish over the years, very few people had had access to the baptismal register housed in the sacristy and, thereby, to any information concerning Ricky Ballistic (*né* Balanciaga) that is contained therein. Three of those people were, of course, the successive Bishops of Salford since Ricky Balanciaga's birth – Bishops Holland, Kelly, and Brain. And we may be sure that, on the occasion of their respective episcopal visitations of the parish of St Joseph of Cupertino, these three churchmen would have concerned themselves with matters of more immediate importance to the church and the Diocese other than in idle speculation about the origins of a man whom (had they even paused to give him a moment's thought) they would have accounted a businessman at best, with a legitimate fortune based in the ice cream trade, and, at worst, an apostate and devotee of a personal hedonistic philosophy (described by some at street level as being 'at it' – 'at' meaning 'deeply involved in'; 'it' meaning 'the trans-shipment and marketing of illegal substances'). Not that any one of the successive Bishops of Salford would have adjudged Ricky Ballistic a hopeless case, of course. For no man's case is a hopeless one until he gives up on himself – or until others of his acquaintance decide it is time they undertook that decision on his behalf.

The only other people allowed access to the mysteries of St Joseph's baptismal register were the successive headteachers of St Joseph of Cupertino's school, the present incumbent being Mr Desmond Aloysius Linsgreave. And, in the spring of 2002 (a couple of months prior to Ricky Ballistics' demise) Mr Linsgreave approached Canon Pavor for details, not of Ricky Ballistic (*né* Balanciaga), but of one, Matthew Casio, putative son of Ricky Ballistic, Matthew Casio being now seven years of age and scheduled to make his First Holy Communion in the company of thirty-two of his classmates.

This is that same Matthew Casio whose proud mother, Francesca Casio, had been entirely dependent on the support of her family in raising the boy consequent upon Ricky Ballistic's denial of any knowledge of the matter despite the fact that, in the autumn of 1994, he had most definitely had knowledge of Francesca Casio in a biblical sense during a late holiday the two of them had enjoyed in Sorrento and Rome, Matthew being born in the summer of 1995.

It was a fine February morning and Mr Linsgreave walked the four blocks from the school to the presbytery, wearing a light grey two-piece suit, a Vyella tie and a pair of Oxford brogues. His spectacles (from Specsave in Middleton Arndale Centre) awaited his attention within a leathern slip-in case in the breast pocket of his jacket whence it was Mr Linsgreave's practice to produce them at strategic moments of emphasis at meetings of teachers, headteachers and parents in a manner that, Mr Lingreave felt, was reminiscent of a bit of business by Gregory Peck stumbling through a homespun Clarence Darrow-like scene in a country court room. Mr Linsgreave's executive case, initialled DAL, ('I'm sorely tempted to add an EK suffix to that,' his wife Bernadette had threatened him, jokingly.) . . . his executive case swung loosely in his left hand as he rang the day-bell at the presbytery with his right.

Mrs Keating answered the door, showing Mr Linsgreave into the waiting-room, where he was leafing sightlessly through a copy of *The Word* when Canon Pavor appeared.

'Oh, it's yeself, Desmond.' Canon Pavor dredged up a few remnants of an accent he had outgrown at the English College, Rome, a lifetime ago. 'Come on through, will ye?'

Linsgreave got to his feet, a subservient smile playing about his lips. He followed the Canon along the passage way, inclining his head marginally so as to diminuate his five foot ten inches height beside the Canon's five foot nine as they passed into a room, the priest's living-room, which was dominated by a monstrous monochrome close-up of Christ's head, crowned with thorns yet sporting a singularly well-barbered Van Dyck beard.

The Canon indicated an armchair near the hearth, well-provided with cushions. 'Take a load off ye feet, man.'

Linsgreave sat down uneasily. 'It's the . . . er . . .' Perching on, rather than sitting in the armchair, Linsgreave drew a sheet of A4 paper from his opened executive case and passed it across to the Canon. 'The, er, the list of First Communicants. I'll need to check the details of baptisms, I mean . . .'

'Mmm.' Canon Pavor hummed appreciatively as he perused the list Linsgreave handed him. 'How many this year, Desmond?'

'Er . . . thirty, thirty-three, Canon.'

'Thirty-*three*? A goodly crop and an apposite number!' The Canon glanced across at Linsgreave above the rim of his spectacles.

Dizzy Dezzy (this was the Canon's private nickname for the man), Dizzy Dezzy was perspiring freely as he invariably did when they met.

The noise in that school! thought the Canon. What a lousy disciplinarian he was! A creep too. (Who but a creep would tolerate that self-opinionated Oxbridge arsehole, Hector Scoffington-Gordale, the LEA inspector, at a family wedding?) . . . Socially inept in many respects too (What kind of a fool would dream of using Mark Antony's speech at Rosemary Troup's retirement party? 'I come to bury Caesar', indeed!) . . . In addition to being nothing other than an ignoramus when it came to spelling. *Practiss*, was it? *Attatch*, eh? *Batchelor* of Education, is she? (Millicent Wytham, this: Linsgreave was a T. Cert.) Even so, he seemed to be well thought of at the Offices. God alone knew why. God in the shape of that insufferable Oxbridge arsehole and gobshite, Hector Scoffington-Gordale, most likely! Ah, well! You had to trust the professionals, hadn't you? Otherwise where were you?

The Canon resumed his study of the list of names. 'Leo Ellison? Is that Bill's lad.'

'I . . . er . . . I believe so, Canon.'

'Oh, what's this? You have a Mathew, Mathew Casio.'

'That's correct, Canon.'

'Ah, but *is* it?. I mean, my own father was Mathew – God rest his soul – but I've never known another.'

'Beg pardon, Canon?'

Canon Pavor slipped his spectacles off and fixed Linsgreave with a frank stare. Then his face relaxed somewhat. 'Forgive an old man, Desmond. I'm afraid I'm not explaining myself very well. What I mean to say is I've known Matthews by the score, of course. That is, Matthew: M, a, double-tee, e, double-yew. But Mathew, one tee? Well, I've only known the one, my own father, Mathew Cathal Pavor. It was one of those family things, you know. And I tell a lie, Desmond, I understand there's a Mathew Street, one tee, in Liverpool that people make a fuss about on Granada Television every now and again. Don't ask me why. And, of course, there's Father Mathew, of course, from my own County Mayo. The apostle of temperance.'

'Canon?'

'Father Mathew from Westport, County Mayo. At least that's where his monument's to be found. The founder of the Pioneer Movement. Still, we won't let the thought detain us any longer, Desmond.' Canon Pavor rose to his feet.'

'Canon?' Linsgreave said again, squirming on, rather than in, his chair. The sweat had begun to gather along his eyebrows. Another second and he would have to get his handkerchief out.

Turning his back on Linsgreave, Canon Pavor went across to the whisky decanter on top of a chest of drawers below the monochrome Christ with the designer beard. He glanced at his wristwatch. Half past two. 'Will ye partake of a wee dram before ye go, Desmond?'

Linsgreave had risen just as swiftly. He gave a quick and quite unnecessary blast in his handkerchief by way of an excuse for having it his hands. 'Er . . . no, no. Er . . . thank you, Canon. Not . . . not during working hours, you know. Some other time perhaps.' Linsgreave essayed a smile.

'Well, just as you please, Desmond. And, in that case, I think I'd best postpone mine till later. Mrs Keating does a lovely fillet of beef of a Wednesday. I'll have mine after that. Well, I'll see you to the door then, and I'll get those details back to you later in the week. Tomorrow maybe.'

'*Liar!*' muttered Canon Pavor under his breath once Linsgreave had departed.

The Canon chuckled. He was delighted to see it had started to rain. Hah! Persisting down, it was. The man would get a thorough soaking on his way back to the school.'

During the Christmas vacation the Canon had been called into the school by Stan Holwick, the caretaker, who was concerned about the central heating boiler breaking down. And when the Canon had himself complained about the biting cold in the building, Stan had unearthed a half-used bottle of Grant's Standfast from the filing cabinet in Linsgreave's office. Canon Pavor laughed to himself as he walked back to his study. As far as he could recall, the bottle of whisky in Linsgreave's office had been filed under 'U'.

For *Uisegebeatha*? The Canon wondered – and not for the first time, mouthing the word. Was it possible the fool could spell in Gaelic but not in English?

'Well, my curiosity's certainly aroused, Don,' said Sergeant Benny Wessenden, taking his place in the queue in the staff canteen and reaching down a plastic tray for himself. 'Think I'll go the full Monty. Sets you up for the rest of the day, I reckon . . . No, do tell, Don. So, what was it in particular that alerted you to the fact that all was not well with Ballistic and Del Monte?'

'Well, for one thing,' said Don Jarvis, reaching down a tray for himself and sorting out some cutlery for the pair of them, two knives, two forks, one spoon: Don didn't take sugar, 'They still do baked beans with the breakfast?' he asked Benny.

'They do whatever you want, boy. I don't suppose there's too many devilled kidneys left at this time o' day – but baked beans, mushrooms, extra egg. No problem.'

'I'll have the same as you, then.'

'Full Monty, Betty,' said Benny. 'Make it two, will you?'

'See, the thing is' – Don Jarvis helped himself to salt and pepper sachets, a paper napkin – 'our friends were parked up at the grill, I mean the pelican. And the lights were on green.'

'The pelican? . . . An' a tea, Betty . . . Don? . . . Two teas, love.'

'Lights at Beech Mount. Across from the Gala Bingo Hall.

227

What used to be the Cintra. Brewster Street, is it? Lights on green, car facing towards town.'

'Struck you as odd, that, did it, Don?'

'Well, wouldn't it you? Two o'clock in the morning, no traffic to speak of, car engine running, lights on friggin' green? And that wasn't all . . . Stick us some baked beans on, will you, Betty? . . . No, that wasn't all. Mycroft would've clocked it. Never mind Sherlock . . .'

'Who?'

'Who *what*?'

'*Who*'d've clocked it?'

'Mycroft Holmes, Sherlock's brother.

'Clocked what?

'Him and her, Ballistic . . .'

'What?'

'Their heads had gone. Well, near as dammit.'

'You mean? Their heads had gone?'

'You think I mean? I don't mean bleedin' dandruff, cocaine-gone; I mean Purdy double-barrel shotgun gone . . . Oh, do us a runny egg, will you, Betty? This one's rock hard . . . Mind you, they hadn't gone far. Christ! There was bits of gunge all over the shop: dashboard, windscreen . . . Thanks, Betty. You're a good un . . . Hey, but the laugh of it was, well, funny anyway, the car radio was still blaring away. Had to turn the damned thing off. Didn't seem right somehow – and I don't care what forensic says about not touching nowt. (And if forensic don't say sawn off shotgun and Mikey The Gun Casio, and brother Donny, I'm on for a twenny-spot.) Hey, too right I turned it off. Wouldn't you? Two stiffs in the motor, people out in the street by this time. Prob'ly got woke up by the noise of the shots . . . and there's Bill Medley and Jennifer Warnes singing 'I've Had the Time of My Life'. Didn't seem right somehow. Leastways not without Patrick Swayze strutting his stuff.'

'You want the HP or the ketchup?' Benny Wessenden asked him, taking a paper napkin to the lip of the HP sauce bottle. 'State of this,' said Benny Wessenden. 'Think they'd give it a bit of a wipe over with a dish cloth now and then, wouldn't you? Here,

Hulbertson . . .' Turning on his heel, Custody Sergeant Benny Wessenden flung the HP sauce bottle, topless, the length of the breakfast queue, etching an ephemeral brown arc in the air that fell instantly to the plastic-tiled floor of the canteen before PC Paul Hulbertson near the back of the queue succeeded in catching it. ' . . . Clean up *cette sauce de haute qualité* for your old sergeant when you've got a minute, will you?' said Custody Sergeant Benny Wessenden.

Junction of Factory Lane/Rochdale Road, 1958 – Golden Tavern to the left; the Top Derby to the right

45

A Dog in a Million: R.I.P.*

You blinked when garden mower
snipped from your tail its tip,
Ah! whimpered as your right hind leg
so swiftly followed it;
Then, Lucky, when it took your head:
you yelped just once, and fell down dead.

* Postcard in the window of Market Stall, Long Street, Middleton,
  Manchester: out 6.6.90; 10p per week; 50p paid in full by Mr C.
  McClintock.

Kitty Dignan's (Hughes by marriage) confectioner's, next door but
one to Ray McGrath's bicycle shop (opposite the new North City
Library and College), 1968

COLORADO

prop. B. Marlfield

New TVs for Old**

Does your TV at home work perfectly well but have
that old-fashioned
teak, mahogany, or walnut look?
Do you want a TV with the modern black finish?
Do you have better things to do with your money than
to go out and spend it on a brand new TV when your
old one is working perfectly?
If so COLORADO TV has the answer!
PHONE US TODAY and discover how we can bring your
old TV bang up-to-date with our AMAZING LOW-COST
SIX STAGE NERONISATION PROCESS!
This offer includes the free loan of a recently
neronised Teletext colour TV while your TV is being
modernised in our workshop.

Tel: COLORADO TV on 643– [blurred; felt tip?] **for a
free quotation without obligation. And remember:
BLACK IS BEAUTIFUL**

---

*   Postcard in the window of Market Stall, Long Street, Middleton, out 12
    months hence, 6.1.85, £5 paid for in full (cash) by Pearson Marlfield

46

Dee-Jay U E Jay in print:

To the *Fiducial Times, Rewind & Revue*:

Sir,
Ref: *The Rise and Fall of Popular Music* by Donald Clarke
Viking, 1995, ISBN 0670832448

Bruce Springsteen's reported remark about Chuck Berry playing 'strange' chords, is far from imbecilic, as your reviewer suggests it is, particularly when placed in the original context in which Springsteen made the remark.

The quote in question comes from a Springsteen interview which, together with contributions from Eric Clapton, Keith Richards *et al.*, are to be found on a marvellous video entitled *Hail, Hail, Rock 'n' Roll**, which gives some revealing insights into Chuck Berry as a performer, and into Springsteen and Richards as enthusiasts for his work.

Keith Richards speculates that, back in the 1950s, Chuck Berry got many of his musical ideas from Johnnie Johnson, a pianist with whose combo Berry was playing at that time in St Louis, Missouri.

Chuck Berry songs, says Richards, are in piano chords whereas a rock guitarist would normally play in A and E and D because of the open strings.

This links in with Bruce Springsteen's comment about 'strange' keys, where Springsteen is in the process of recalling how he and his group once stood in as Chuck Berry's backing group though in doing so, they were up against two distinct disadvantages: a) Berry arrived on stage at the very last minute; and b) proceeded to perform without divulging either a song title or a musical key to his accompanists.

Of course, there is so much more than this to the video. Springsteen's boyish enthusiasm is wonderful to behold, as are Keith Richards' efforts to get Chuck Berry (reportedly a tightwad

232

who's not fast with a buck) to perform on stage with a properly rehearsed band.

But thanks for the book review, especially since it prompted me to re-run an eminently re-watchable video.

Yours,

Eugene Jameson
Bar Barbarossa
Playa de Las Americas, Tenerife
14 February 1997

To *You Don't Say*, the *Daily Mess*

Sir,

Rock Concerts in Manchester

At 15 years of age I well remember demanding my money back from the box office at the Odeon, Oxford Street, when Mark Wynter was substituted for Jerry Lee Lewis whose marriage to a child bride had offended public taste overnight. And, age 22, I witnessed Little Richard's spectacular full-throated lap of honour round this same auditorium, upstairs and down.

Sadly, the Rolling Stones I coughed up my hard-earned cash to see *circa* 1963 had only a handful songs in their repertoire at the time, subsequent to which performance I endured what must surely have been the most begrudgingly mean-spirited public performance of Chuck Berry's professional career.

Generally speaking though, rock shows at the Odeon represented good value for money (*e.g.* an Everly Brothers' concert with Bo Diddley on the same bill). In any case, there's no way the Odeon had a monopoly on class acts.

The Kinks appeared at The Bodega on Cross Street; The Big O at the Domino Club, Grey Mare Lane – and I saw The

Merseybeats at the World Famous Embassy Club and St Bernadette's, Withington.

St Bernadette's, in fact, made a bid to book The Beatles back in 1963, but baulked at the booking fee. I well remember this being adjudged so exorbitant by a friend of mine (nowadays a well-respected member of the judiciary), that it caused him to cast doubt on the respective parentage of John, Paul, George and Ringo – and of Brian Epstein too.

Yep – when it came to rock concerts, as with everything else, we Mancunians expected value for money, and those thieving Scousers wanted eighty quid!

In retrospect, I find this positively breathtaking, though I hesitate to say in which respect.

Yours,

Eugene Jameson
Bar Barbarossa
Playa de Las Americas, Tenerife
Canary Islands
January 2005

47

Yvonne Hardiker (*née* Bateman)

She was three years old now and she was a *BIG* girl and if she was a *VERY* big girl and put her teddy bear nightie on like Mamma had told her to do and got into bed now Mamma had dried her hair, well, Daddy would come up and see her before she went to sleep and say night-night and tell her a story.

But she had to be *GOOD*.

So she did what Mamma had said. She took the teddy bear nightie Mamma had given her, *HER* teddy bear nightie – and the teddy bear nightie was nice and warm from where Mamma had been airing it on the fireguard in front of the coal fire in the living-room. Mmm, her teddy bear nightie was nice and warm and she held it up against her cheek . . . and, oh, she could have gone to sleep right there where she stood – yes, gone to sleep right there, standing on the rug with the curly-wurly pattern and the pinky spots. But she was a big girl now, so she slipped her right arm inside the sleeve of her teddy bear nightie and then realised she had done it wrong because it was back to front now. So she took her arm out of the sleeve and did it the right way and shoved her head through the neck hole too and tidied her hair with a few quick flicks, pushing it away from her face with both hands so that it fell to her shoulders, and she jumped up then and got on to the bed next to Nelly Kelly.

'You gotta be big girl, Nelly,' she told Nelly Kelly. 'You gotta be *VERY* big girl and get in bed and Daddy come see you, tell a story.'

She plonked Nelly Kelly on the pillow right up against the headboard and covered her up so that only Nelly's button-eyes were showing and the top of her pipe-cleaner hair and then she climbed in next to Nelly Kelly and covered herself up, pulling the winceyette sheet right up to her chin and folding it back so she wouldn't be able to feel the other blankets, the grey ones and the brown one that had stitching along the top and bottom edges, and she pulled her eiderdown up too so it was level with the top of the winceyette sheet. Then she lay back with her eyes wide-open, waiting for Daddy to come, watching the bedroom door for when Daddy would come through it, and – while she waited for Daddy to come – she looked all around her bedroom where, because it was on the street side at the front of the house, she would sometimes hear footsteps on the pavement at night when people walked past the window or people came talking and whistling and sometimes shouting down the street.

'Judd-oh!' she had heard a man shout last night from across the street near Ye Golden Lion. 'Judd-*oh*!' And then there had been footsteps. But not tonight. There was nobody shouting tonight. There was just Billy Wind, and Billy Wind would blow something against the window sometimes, something like a wire or a string or a stick. She didn't know what it was. 'Tick!' it would go. And it was frightening, though not as frightening as Harry Hailstones or Jack Thunder

There was a night light on the bedside cabinet next to her bed, and there was a sticky teaspoon and a bottle of Tyxylyx as well. Mamma had had to give her a spoonful of Tyxylyx last night when she woke up coughing. On the shelf below the Tyxylyx she could see her new *Rupert* Annual that Father Christmas had brought her and her Toby Twirl book and the comic with Tiger Tim in it. The back of the little chair next to the bedside cabinet held her frock and her socks and her ribbons and her knickers and her vest and her liberty bodice, ready for morning; and her shoes (her Bobby Shaftoe buckle shoes, Mamma said they were) were on the floor underneath the little chair. All her other clothes – her undies (Mamma called them), her jim-jams (Mamma, again), her hankies, her socks, ribbons, gaiters, gloves and mittens – these were all in the top drawer of the tall boy that had some of Mamma's things in the next drawer down, and the photograph album in the third drawer down with photographs of Mamma and Daddy in it and Grandma and Grandpa and her other Grandma and her other Grandpa who was up in heaven now and Daddy and Mamma with Uncle Gerald and Auntie Gloria and other grown-up people she didn't know, all laughing, and then a baby in a cot and a baby in Mamma's arms and a baby trying to walk and a baby with

Mamma and Daddy in *Bucket* Hole Clough. And the baby was her, Yvonne Catherine Bateman. The baby was her, Mamma said. And Mamma said Yvonne Catherine Bateman wasn't a baby any more, because *HER* Yvonne was a BIG girl now, Mamma said. Yes, she was. She was a *VERY* big girl. Because she could put her teddy bear *NIGHTIE* on all by herself and get into *BED* all by herself . . . Why, she could even *DRESS* herself in the morning when Mamma told her to and buckle her Bobby Shaftoe buckle shoes and very nearly tie the shoelaces on her Sunday shoes and brush her hair and . . .

She giggled, hearing Daddy's footsteps on the stairs. One . . . two . . . three . . . four – she counted – five . . . seven . . . ten . . . She counted a lot of footsteps, and then she heard Daddy on the landing and saw the bedroom door opening . . . open . . . and Daddy coming through it, smiling, in his uniform still – his shirt and tie and trousers, but not the great big coat with the great big lapels Daddy had been wearing when he came marching up the street from the 26 bus stop this afternoon with the big bag on his shoulder and the cap on his head.

'Where's my big . . . where's my big . . . oh, where's my big big girl?' said Daddy, hugging her, loving her – giving her such a squeeze all her breath seemed to leave her at once.

She giggled.

Daddy smelled of cigarettes and coffee and hair tonic and orange peel and chocolate and walnuts and Brazil nuts and dates and something hot as fire and smelling of Christmas. Daddy was big; Daddy was big like the giant in her Jack the Giant-Killer pop-up story book that Father Christmas had brought her from Uncle Gerald and Auntie Gloria. Daddy was so big, and not soft like mamma was soft. But daddy was soft in his own way when he held her and hugged her and squeezed her, leaving his arms loose so she could move and pull herself free and move about and move away from him and jump down when she wanted to.

Daddy said: 'Mmm! I'm going to eat you all up!' And Daddy said Yvonne Catherine Bateman was the Princess Snow White and needn't be afraid when The Woodman took her into the woods because the Seven Dwarves would find her and take her to their home with them deep inside the forest where she could stay with them and be safe for ever and a day. And Yvonne Catherine Bateman, aged 3, aka the Princess Snow White, heard everything Daddy told her until a Handsome Prince got into the story, at which point Yvonne Bateman's eyes 'shut off' (as she called dropping off to sleep). So Daddy covered her up then and kissed her once more and left the night light on and went out and closed the bedroom door after him.

'*You're* not my daddy,' she had said to Asa that time. She smiled to herself, remembering it. How old had she been when she had said that to Asa? Five? Six? No, it was New Year's Eve, wasn't it? It was the New Year's Eve when Asa and Mum were going to the fancy dress party. Yes, she must have been seven, and she was being naughty for the baby-sitter, Asa's niece, Ursula. So Asa, dressed as Robin Hood for the party, tried to reason with her.

'You're not *my* Mummy and Daddy,' she told him. 'You're The Woo'man. You can't tell me what to do.'

'Wha'd yer mean, I'm a woman?' said Asa, mishearing her.

'You're The Woo'man . . . you're The Woo'man . . . you're The Woo'man . . .' She said it over and over again until mum, Maid Marian, stepped in and smacked her.

She threw her *School Friend* comic down now, remembering it. But why ever should she think of it at this moment? Maybe it was the sound of the New Year's Eve party going on downstairs that had brought it to mind, she thought – the laughter (a bit too hilarious), the giggling, voices drifting up the stairs from time to time, the occasional shouting and catcalls (the women shrilly, the men indistinctly and gruff), the thump of the bass from the music playing loudly on the Ekco radiogram in the living-room.

Mum and Asa had treated themselves to the Ekco radiogram for Christmas and to half a dozen 78 rpm records to go with it. The radiogram came from Fred Dawes on Rochdale Road, facing Christ Church; the records from Mrs Wykes's shop on Moston Lane. Mum and Asa had bought one record every week for the last six weeks, stopping off at Mrs Wykes's shop in between shopping at Armistead's baker's shop and Estall's grocer's shop on a

Saturday morning. And, that night, between half past eight (when everybody began turning up) till the stroke of midnight – which the Westclox alarm clock on top of her bedroom cabinet told her it was now all of fourteen minutes past – they must have played those half dozen records a dozen times each at least.

'Why Do Fools Fall In Love?' by Frankie Lymon and the Teenagers (everyone went 'oo-wah, oo-wah' to that one), 'Whatever Will Be' by Doris Day (to which they all sang two words of Italian), 'Lay Down Your Arms' by Anne Shelton (one or two of the guests pretended they had mistaken the word 'arms' for another, ruder, word and insisted on playing Musical Chairs to it), 'When Mexico Gave Up The Rhumba' by Mitchell Toruk (which gave rise to a travesty of Latin American dancing), 'Singing The Blues' by Tommy Steele and 'Green Door' by Frankie Vaughan (these last two records prompting a bit of inexpert yodelling).

They were all grown-ups at mum and Asa's New Year's Eve party and they were all being completely stupid. That is, they were all being completely stupid in a different kind of way to the way in which Yvonne Bateman and Estelle Hanlith and their friends would have all been completely stupid if they had been allowed to have a New Year's Eve Party of their own. That's why she had come up to bed. Because she was bored.

She knew it was going to be boring, having no friends of her own there, or anyone of her own age, and with all the grown-ups drinking too much and thinking they were all so very funny – hah, hah, hah – and great Latin American dancers and singers and Italian linguists, or whatever it was they thought they were good at; and with Asa fooling around all night long, wearing the light shade off the standard lamp at one stage and pretending to be a Chinaman (or, 'a Chinee', as Asa would say, this being Asa's idea of the word 'Chinese' in the singular).

'Estelle's coming for your birthday on Sunday. So, no,' Mum had told her when Yvonne had asked if Estelle Hanlith could come to the New Year's Eve Party.'

So that was that. There was nothing more to be said. And the party had been boring just like she had expected it to be. So she had stuck it out till half-past eleven and then she had come up to bed before 'Auld Lang Syne'. Oh, you just *bet* she had. Yvonne had come up to bed to *avoid* 'Auld Lang Syne' and all that pawing, and the clingy, singing, smoochy stuff. Yeah, you just *bet* she had.

She had a quick wash and she sat on the bed and after a while she lay down on the bed in her long pyjama top and her dressing-gown and with the pillow punched into a nice firm shape right up against the headboard, resting her head on it and reading *School Friend*. She wouldn't have been able to get to sleep with all the noise downstairs in any case – thirty people making it sound as if there were three hundred of them singing 'Auld Lang Syne'.

The oil-filled radiator had been on all night, taking the chill off her bedroom and it hadn't been a cold night in the first place. So, she lay on top of the bed, reading, until she remembered Asa dressed as Robin Hood all those years ago and mum smacking her, so she threw her *School Friend* comic down in temper then and picked up *Picturegoer* magazine instead and began to flick through it, pausing to read about Tab Hunter. Then she just lay there for a while with the lamp switched on and the magazine falling from her hands now and her eyes growing heavy, then closing, despite the singing and the shouting and the clumping up the stairs and then down again and the banging of the front door as Mum and Asa's guests began to leave.

Every so often her eyes would open fractionally and she'd look around the room, and then they'd close again. Then one time – maybe the tenth time she had opened her eyes like this. She didn't know: she didn't know when it was. But one time when she opened her eyes, Asa was standing there, looking at her, looking down at her in a way she didn't like.

'Hap' 'Oo Year, swee'ar',' he said indistinctly, seeing her open her eyes to him and blink.

Somewhat unsteadily, Asa put the wineglass he was holding on the bedside cabinet between the table lamp and the Westclox alarm clock, and, as he did so, he leaned towards her and across her, making a fumbling attempt to kiss her.

She turned her face from him instinctively, dug her heels into the eiderdown to push herself back.

'Aw, c'mo', swee'ie!' said Asa, closer now, breathing wine fumes in her face. 'Is a' a way-a trea' your Da'? Jus' 'ay Hap' 'Oo Year t' Asa wi' li' kiss.'

'No . . . *No*, you're *drunk.*' She was up on her elbows now, clutching at her dressing-gown as it fell apart.

Asa smelled of beer and wine and whisky and cough candy and mince pies and cigarette smoke and cigar smoke and peppery aftershave. Asa, chuckling now, leaned closer still – and fell . . . *fell on top of her.* It was a drunk's fall: Asa had simply lost his footing. The glossy *Picturegoer* magazine, Tab Hunter smiling broadly from its front cover, lay open at his feet, serving to topple him from the vertical to the horizontal so that he fell on her, fell across her – *heavily*, his chuckles expiring in a grunt.

'Get off me, get off me, get *off*!'

Asa did *not* get off her. For a moment it seemed as if he might do so. But then he pushed himself even closer to her – *Agh!* – nuzzled her, dammed an incipient scream with his mouth; and *kept* that scream dammed. Calculatedly now, deliberately too – twice her weight, his limbs knowing greater strength – Asa imprisoned her within his stronger arms, by means of his stronger legs, beneath his sheer, immoveable body weight.

Writhing, quite unable to extricate herself, helpless beneath Asa's bulk, Yvonne could only gasp, not scream: 'Get off me . . . get off me, get *off*!'

In vain!

Asa's mouth made murmurs of her gasps, made mumblings of her murmurs, dimmed her mumblings to one continuous moan of protest. 'Oh . . . Asa . . . far too heavy for . . . oh . . . Asa . . . far too heavy . . . oh . . . Asa was . . . The Woodman . . . oh . . . Asa was the . . . WOULD. . . oh . . . Asa was . . . THE WOODMAN . . . oh . . . Asa was the . . . HEAVY FOR . . . oh . . . Asa FAR TOO HEAVY for . . . HER . . .'

When Asa released her finally, it was not at Yvonne's bidding. No, Asa released her — his hand clasping her mouth tightly – when he *chose* to release her. And Asa took his own good time about doing so. And when Asa released her, and got up off her, and got off the bed, and adjusted his dress, her face was tear-stained and she was sobbing as if her breath had left her and she would never be able to get it back. And when Asa – reaching for the wineglass now, and unsteady on his feet still – seemed as if he would lean across her once more, her lips parted to give vent to the scream of screams. And Asa, seeing her intention in her eyes a millisecond before she could scream, hit her twice across the face, hard and harder . . . so hard, in fact, that she was shocked out of uttering a sound.

'Bitch!' hissed Asa, stumbling against the bedside cabinet with the force of those blows and spilling red wine from his wine glass, which shorted the bedside lamp. 'Breathe a word an' I'll kill you! I mean it, bitch – I'll fuckin'-well kill you, I will!'

And at this point, Yvonne Hardiker (*née* Bateman), fourteen years of age on Sunday next, got between the covers on her bed and pulled them all the way up to the top of her head and lay there sobbing in the darkness. Then, out in the street, across Lion Street near Ye Golden Lion, somebody shouted twice: 'Mark-oh! *Mark-oh!*'

Asa had gone now but, that night and for many nights and for many years after, Yvonne Hardiker (*née* Bateman) would still hear the sound of Asa's laboured breathing in her nightmares and her dreams.

Ghoul Friend

How do I love thee? Let me count the ways:
I love thee with thy thermals off, thy falsies stowed away;
I love thee with thy curlers in; thy Steradented reef,
Not in the glass beside thy pit, but in thy gob beneath.
I love thee with thy smashed pot leg; I love thee with thine hook
I love thee in the eventide with thy five o'clock shadow look
I love thee in the midnight hour when curs attack thy doors
Enragéd by the pungence of thy suppurating sores
I love to touch thine acne- éd brow, thy pachydermal skin
I love to see thee smile at me with conjunctival squint
I love to hear thee bawl to me, distant from the loo:
'Oi! Fetch the Air-Wick: this place stinks
Like Belle Vue-effin'-Zoo
I love to kiss thy warts and boils, caress thy foul carbuncle . . .
(Quick! . . .
                    Un-zip . . .
                                        Thine overalls
Purloinéd from thine uncle.)
I love to pat thy withered hand when shrieketh-thou in frenzy,
See David Beckham looking on in ill-disguiséd envy.
I love to climb extension ladder, peck thy scaly gob;
I love to dodge thy cleaver that thou, oft times thoughtless, lob
I love to catch sweet-nothings thou grunteth basso profundo
But most of all I'll love thee dear when thou art six feet under.

Marlfield Immobiliaria

To *You Don't Say,* the *Daily Mess:*

Sir,

Ref: Where's the justice in this?

A gang of armed robbers gets tooled up with all manner of offensive weapons, remorselessly terrorises the North-West of England with 20 robberies over a two year period, gets away with a haul of more than £250,000, and gets banged up for a total of 78 years. Quite right too!

Or is it?

A Big Issue seller offers no violence whatsoever, defrauds a pensioner of £125, and gets one day in gaol for every pound she took. Some people have written in to say the Big Issue seller should have got a stiffer sentence, but there are two things these people have overlooked.

If the courts had treated the armed robbers as viciously as the Big Issue seller, they'd have got 666 years in all. And if the Big Issue seller had been treated as leniently as the armed robbers, she'd have been out in a fortnight.

Obviously, poverty is regarded as the more reprehensible crime in this town, and readers who may be interested in a life of crime will be quick to notice that the justices prefer villains to go in hard and go for broke.

Yours,

Byron Marlfield
Refuge Building, Manchester

[DATE UNCLEAR: COFFEE STAIN] 2000

Hollow Wishes

His shoes are the slip-on type, black in colour, leather – good, soft
Italian leather selected for him by his wife Bernadette during their
stay with her cousin, Sean (now Bishop Malchus) in Assisi last
summer. They have tassels to each instep and rubber to each
heel – heels which were subsequently rendered intentionally
unquiet by his personal attachment to them of a pair of half-moon
shaped metal studs on the last that was his father's (when they
lived on Belper Street, Harpurhey, and he himself was a pupil at St
Edmund's RC Primary School on Monsall Street) and a hammer
(loose upon its shaft now) that had originally belonged to his
grandfather, the cobbler. His suit – the trousers retaining a crease
where there should be a crease but with creases too to the knees
and crotch; the jacket buttoned, a red Bic ballpoint pen peeping
above the parapet of its top pocket – his suit is light-grey in
colour, herringbone-patterned in texture. Like a Ken Dodd stage
suit, thinks Bernadette, one eye on the clock (half-past one
already), a dull suit, vapid, sartorially uninspired – serving (in Ken
Dodd's case, certainly) as a backdrop to a major event that is in
the offing at any moment now, and people have paid good money
to see. A claret-coloured pocket handkerchief, intended (by
Bernadette, earlier this morning) to complement the Viyella tie she
bought for him on their daughter's behalf on Fathers' Day,
knowing it would never occur to their daughter to buy him a gift,
has long since (since morning break, to be precise) been re-
consigned from top pocket to his right-hand trouser pocket and,
from time to time, to his nose, serving as a receptacle for the
occasional detritus of a slight head cold that has come upon him
me subsequent to his exiting the Lancashire Health and Racquets
Club on Heywood Old Road at five minutes past eight this
morning and switching on the ignition of his Mazda 626 GXi
saloon. He (the man in question) being Mr Desmond Aloysius
Linsgreave, alumnus of De La Salle College, Pendleton, of St
Mary's Training College, Strawberry Hill: hence a Simmarian
(and a 'Cimmerian' too on one occasion – ha, ha – when

Bernadette happened to have *Chambers Twentieth Century Dictionary* ready to hand), and officially, Mr D. A. Linsgreave, T. Cert.

'*Cack, cack, cack, cack, cack,*' says Matthew Casio under his breath, on the ground floor corridor, standing opposite the door to Mr Linsgreave's office, essaying vocal reproduction of the noise Mr Linsgreave's heels make as he strides authoritatively (as is Mr Linsgreave's wont) along that same ground floor corridor to the door of his office, which he enters without speaking.

Mr Linsgreave's shoes are clean, though not sparkling clean; his suit – fresh (courtesy of Bernadette, one week since) from the dry-cleaning concession at C&L News on the Kirkway roundabout in Alkrington – never does look clean exactly. Uncreased is the best Desmond's suit ever looks, uncreased and uncluttered, thinks Bernadette, sitting at the table nearest the door in Mr Thomas's, gazing through the window towards the water, her coffee growing colder by the minute, today's *Daily Mess* folded in half on the gingham tablecloth before her, unread, apart from the quarter page advertisement for Chatleys Warehouse. Why couldn't he go down to Cheetham Hill like she wanted him to and buy himself a new suit for work? Bernadette looks once more at the Chatleys Warehouse advertisement in the *Daily Mess*. Why on earth *couldn't* he?

'*Cuh, cuh, cuh, cuh, cuh.*' Matthew Casio's trainers – the Buzz Lightyear trainers with the flashing lights in the heels, a birthday present from his uncle, Mikey (Mikey The Gun) Casio, upon his release from police custody the previous Friday – Matthew Casio's Buzz Lightyear trainers make a different, less impressively resonant sound on the composite flooring of the ground floor corridor. '*Cug, cug, cug, cug, cug*' is the best Matthew Casio heels can come up with. But the light show the trainers afford – amber, red, red, red, amber, red – is nothing less than semi-spectacular to a child's eyes in the semi-gloom of the ground floor corridor of St Joseph of Cupertino RC Primary School at twenty-five minutes to two on the afternoon of the Thursday of Holy Week, with St Joseph of Cupertino RC Primary

School due to break up in one hour fifty-five minutes time for the Easter holiday, and a complement of just two children on the ground floor corridor at this point in time.

'Yer doin', Cazz-oh?' Christopher Stanegate, Matthew Casio's classmate, on his way to the office with Mrs Wytham's afternoon register under his arm, avails himself of a Mancunian vernacular forbidden to him at home by his mother, Dr Stanegate's wife, Siobhan. 'Cazz-oh! What yer doin'?'

'*Cuh-cug, cuh-cug, cuh-cug,*' say Matthew Casio's heels by way of reply – red, red, red, amber, red, red.

Christopher Stanegate laughs.

'*Ba-nanas in py-jam-as are com-ing down the stairs,*' sing Mrs Wytham's girls in Junior Two. '*Ba-nanas in py-jamas are com-ing down in pairs . . . .*'

'*Cuh-cug-cuh-cug, cuh-cug-cuh-cug, cuh-cug-cuh-cug-cuh-cug,*' say Matthew Casio's heels by way of accompaniment, the light show they provide repetitively resplendent.

Matthew Casio has been standing on the corridor across from Mr Linsgreave's office since ten minutes past noon today, a garden pea flicked skywards on first sitting the cause . . .

. . . The cause too of Mrs Agnes Scuggins, one of the school dinner supervisors, wishing 'Mr Linsgreave would sort these boys out once and for all' – and saying as much to the other three dinner supervisors and half a dozen dinner ladies, sitting down to their dinners in the school hall now the children are back in class. Not to put too fine a point on it, Mrs Agnes Scuggins further expresses the wish, half a suet dumpling stopping, forked, just short of her open mouth, that 'they'd bring back the strap, they would'. Whilst the cook, Mrs Mairead Maureen McCorquodale – mindful perhaps of certain cruel instruments of martial law imposed upon her forbears, the survivors of Vinegar Hill, 1798 – herself a survivor of three headteachers at St Joseph of Cupertino RC Primary School: Fred Swellands, Sally McKay, Desmond Linsgreave (though she's 'not survived that yoke just yet', as her husband Tadgh reminded her subsequent to last year's First Communion breakfast fiasco) – yes, Mrs Mairead Maureen

McCorquodale, the last of the ladies to sit down to her dinner today, plonks her plate of stew (two ladlefuls) and dumplings (ten) down on the table, with a noise reminiscent of a judge's gavel, and declares 'Sure, Oi wish't dey'd bring back de cat, Oi do. Because dere's no dealin' wid 'em nowadays. 'S' like ever'tin's a game t'wum!'

Best game yet, thinks Matthew Casio. This is something! *'Cuh-cuh-cuh-cug, cuh-cuh-cuh-cug . . .'* Well, it's better than plucking the leaves one by one from the Busy-Lizzies in the plant troughs next to Mr Linsgreave's office door until no leaves remain . . . Better than nutting the trophy cupboard above the plant troughs and making the Charles Wessenden Memorial Trophy rattle and tilt . . . Better than running at the Trophy Cupboard wall and kicking off it at a height of three foot six on a level with (Vinny Irlam's retirement gift to the school) the Guiseley sandstone holy water font bearing the inscription VIVA CRISTO REY whilst shout-whispering: 'Spiderma-a-a-an!' Yeah, this is something!

Something? Yes, there certainly *is* something. Mr Linsgreave knows it for a fact. Something he should be doing, something he fully intended to do. But the trouble is that he cannot for the life of him remember what it is.
Mackerel Gutting for Middle Infants?
No, it's not that.
A problem having arisen with the plastic knives the stores department has sent out, Hector has promised he'll sort that out. Hector has given him his solemn word of honour that he will certainly sort things out for the first week of the summer term at the latest. Hector Scoffington-Gordale, MA (Oxon.), that is – aka Hector Crass, to the salaried minions of the education service, that is, to the *hoi polloi* of the education service from class teacher level down – Hector Scoffington-Gordale, MA (Oxon.) being the LEA Inspector responsible for Educational Initiatives and also District Inspector and, as such, the perennial professional benefactor of Desmond Aloysius Linsgreave, T. Cert., subsequent to and consequent upon Mr Linsgreave's studied, eloquent, and

consistent espousal of Scoffington-Gordale-sponsored educational initiatives down the years. Currently this extends to the aforesaid *Mackerel Gutting for Middles* (apropos of which Mr Linsgreave is hopeful of Hector's arranging for the necessary implements to be delivered on time as promised), *Tug-o'-War for Top Infants* (last year's initiative) and, way back in history now – and the very first time their paths had crossed, Linsgreave and Crass – *Flower Arranging for the Under Fives*, the precursor of all subsequent educational initiatives, when Linsgreave had merely been Head of Topiary at St Osram's and, on the occasion of the inaugural Baker Day meeting for the aforesaid *Flower Arranging*, that tosser McClintock from St Joseph's had shown . . . well, his *tosser*, as a matter of fact. Yes, he'd shown it to all and sundry, leaving St Joseph's deputy headship up for grabs for anybody (as Mr Linsgreave truly is, was, and ever shall be) hell-bent upon personal professional advancement. Yes, Hector had been *exceedingly* good to him over the years. Mr Linsgreave smiles, recalling his long and happy association with Hector Scoffington-Gordale, until he remembers again the promised mackerel-gutting knives that have failed to turn up as yet. At which points Lingreave mutters to himself: 'I only wish Hector would get it sorted out as he promised me he'd do.'

'I only wish he'd get it sorted out as he promised me he'd do.'
    'Eh?'
    'Base *Alloy*' – as Scoffington-Gordale now laughingly refers to his acolyte in his cups, and – 'Yes, I'll have No. 11, if you wouldn't mind, please!' – selecting dim-sum as a second course from the menu at the Chanticleer public house in Didsbury Village in the company of P. P. Poontang, M. A. (Cantab.), LEA Inspector for Vehicular Vexillology. 'Stores delivers the wrong utensils as you might well expect of Stores, so Base Alloy faithfully promised me he'll sort the matter out.'
    'You don't pronounce it like that,' says P. P. Poontang, known colloquially amongst the aforementioned salaried minions of the education service as Percy Pedantic, though he is, more correctly stated, Parsee, not Percy.

'Mackerel? Dim-sum? What don't you pronounce like that?'

'Aloysius.' P. P. Poontang accepts with a smile the plate of smoked salmon the waiter sets before him. ' Desmond *Alo-ysius* Linsgreave.'

Scoffington-Gordale fetches up a stirrup-cup laugh along with a stifled belch, spilling – as he does so – a smidgeon of Hirondelle from the fluted wine glass beside his right hand on the tabletop. 'You think I don't know that, Percy?' He dabs at the spillage with a paper napkin. 'I jest, of course. Apropos of which, I wonder if Base Alloy's got the Latin. Because dim *sum* just about sums the silly bugger up!'

'Thought you got on like a house on fire, the two of you.' P. P. Poontang forks smoked salmon mouthwards, thinking about the Melba syllabub with which he is tempted to follow it.

'Oh, we do, old man, we do, ' Scoffington-Gordale coughs, preventing a wad of bread roll dunked in lark's tongue and coriander soup going down the wrong way, coughs again, chuckles. 'Just as long as I've got hold of the ruddy ladder, we do!'

'Ladder?' In the quadrangle outside the office, Linsgreave notices the window cleaner's ladder leaning against the gymnasium wall, half-hidden by the still-flowering cherry tree that was planted on the occasion of the opening of the nursery annexe in 1994 by Councillor Bill Risby, who was the Lord Mayor of Manchester at the time . . . *'Prunus Persica,'* as Fr Brian Seale, the Lord Mayor's chaplain, so described the tree to his congregation at the 11.30 Mass at St John Vianney's church that Bernadette Linsgreave attended the following Sunday, saying (Fr Brian) that he was of a mind to have a second collection on the grounds that he had 'come across a very good gardener during the past week, Councillor Bill Risby, it so happens (*Laughter*), and Bill was of the opinion that a specimen of *Prunus Persica* would be just the thing at the front of St John Vianney's church, and that a *Prunus subhirtella Autumnalis* wouldn't look too bad in the presbytery garden either. Though on reflection, maybe not,' Fr Brian also said, because his 'housekeeper [Miss Sheila Kelly] would very likely tie a washing

line to it before you could say *Prunus Persica,* never mind *Prunus subhirtells Autumnalis.'* (*Laughter*)

Must send a message round about the window cleaners, thinks Linsgreave. Wouldn't do to leave things unattended. Lock the PC software away, hardware too. But it isn't that. No. There's something else he needs to do. But what is it? Mr Linsgreave can't remember. Even so, he cannot shake the feeling that he should be doing something.

Casio maybe? Matthew Casio, cooling his heels out on the corridor – well, cooling his heels as much as the improvised flamenco Matthew Casio has chosen to indulge in for the last five minutes of his ninety minute detention on the ground floor corridor will permit him to cool his heels.

Linsgreave opens his office door on a whim and barks at Matthew Casio out on the corridor. 'CASIO! STOP THAT RACKET!

Christopher Stangate, off-sighted from Linsgreave, exiting the school secretary's room minus Mrs Wytham's class register, snorts with laughter, unheard by Linsgreave, who has retreated to his office again as immediately as he appeared from it. 'What's Lingo done you for, Cazz-oh?'

'Flickin' peas on first sittin',' Matthew Casio clicks his heels once each – amber, red – as he imparts this information.

'Yer'll be stood there till home time then,' opines Christopher Stanegate.. 'When Ikey an' Tigger flushed the broken bog, they was stood there for a week.'

'A *week?'* (Amber)

'Every dinnertime for a week.'

Amber, red: *cuh-cug!*

'STOP THAT NOISE, I SAID!' bawls Linsgreave behind the closed door of his office where the minute hand and the second hand of the Westclox wall clock above the bookcase now coincide with the figure eight.

Something. Mm – something important too, Linsgreave is sure of it. Not the Mackerel Gutting, not the window cleaners, not Matthew Casio. (Has Casio's baptism certificate been ratified yet? Must check that, First Communions coming on apace now. When is it this year? Sunday after Trinity?)

251

Linsgreave flops into his office chair – swivel chair, high back, arms, black leather – swings the seat from side to side as if to calm himself, reaches across to the telephone on the console to the left-hand side of his mahogany desk top, at which point a Size 5 Mouldmaster football bounces once against the office window before someone begins to kick it hard against the window wall.

BUL-LUNG – skit, skitter! BUL-LUNG – skit, skitter!

Immediately up on his feet, Linsgreave storms round his desk, throws open the window, and shouts to the ball-kicking culprit without:

'MULLANEY! WHAT'RE YOU DOING OUT OF CLASS, LAD?'

(Sound of a child's voice, plaintive, apologetic, the words muffled, indistinct.)

'WELL, TAKE THE BALL *BACK* TO MR TAMBURRO. AND GET YOUR TROUSERS ON!'

Not bothering to circumnavigate the desk again, Linsgreave flicks the communicating button on the telephone from where he stands. Better with the window open anyway. Hot in here. He loosens his tie, throws off his jacket, speaks into the telephone receiver. 'Mrs Middleton . . . Oh, Deirdre . . . Yes, I wonder . . . Could you check the Appointments Book, see if I've got anything on later – this afternoon, this evening maybe?'

This *evening*? With the school shut for the Easter *holiday*? With Mass scheduled for half-past six?

Idiot!

Deirdre Middleton knows perfectly well – knows without looking – that there is nothing in the Appointments Book. For tonight anyway. Still, let's have a look at the afternoon, thinks Deirdre Middleton – in the job nineteen years, Mrs McKay's appointment, long-suffering since Linsgreave's appointment twelve years before, and presently engaged, before this unwelcome interruption, in totalling and balancing eight class registers (for the half day, the day, the week, the half-term, the term), plus various monies that have been delivered to her desktop since nine o'clock this morning (dinner money, tuck shop receipts, instalment payments for school uniform, for First Communicants' veils, shirts, socks, ties, medals and ribbons; plus the final receipts for the Delta-Echo Easter card sales). And all of this prior to Deirdre Middleton's scheduled end-of-term trip to the Trustee Savings Bank on Hollinwood Avenue before she'll be able to call it a day.

Hmm!

At least Sally McKay – thinks Deirdre Middleton, reaching for the Appointments Book (under the Disease Book: have to send that round yet) – at least Mrs McKay for all her faults, at least she always made a point of passing across to Deirdre Middleton for her own personal use the "£10-worth of ASDA vouchers per 500 cards" that came as a personal Thank-You for the in-school organiser of greeting card sales, courtesy of Delta-Echo

Hmm, indeed!

And who'd pocketed the ASDA vouchers for the last eleven years? For the Christmas cards too – and we certainly shift some of them. The question is rhetorical, of course. Because Deirdre Middleton knows full well who, these eleven years past, has been shopping occasionally free, or at least partially-free, at ASDA, compliments of Delta-Echo's vouchered appreciation of greetings card sales at St Joseph of Cupertino RC Primary School.

'*NOT* a *SINGLE* thing,' says Deirdre Middleton tartly, employing for this purpose that antiseptic, freeze-you-in-your-tracks, don't-you-*dare*-say-another-word-to-me, sub-screeching tone of voice she learned whilst working as Dr Dryburn's receptionist during the Asian Flu epidemic of the early '60s. Deirdre Middleton slams the telephone receiver down in the privacy of the secretary's office, before translating into the vernacular: 'Not a sausage!'

'Sweet FA! That's what!' says Harry Stanton Holwick, the school caretaker, son of Harry – the eldest son, as it happens: Stan being the one who served ten years with the Manchester Regiment, mainly overseas: this to his wife Valerie, serving up baked beans on toast for his dinner, and for Stan's German Shepherd Belize's dinner too.

253

'Get a break-in at the school one night,' Stan's been heard to observe over his pint of mixed (Boddingtons' bitter and John Willie's Mild) in St Joseph's parish club on occasion, 'An' I hope to Christ it's the Gingerbread Man, dog that's a vegetarian, who ever heard of such a thing!'

In the living-room of the school bungalow next to the David Lewis Recreation Ground on Tudor Avenue Stan gets stuck into the four rounds of toast and six spoonfuls of baked beans that Valerie sets before him – Smart Price in each instance, both items from ASDA, Pilsworth, where Stan runs Valerie every Thursday night to do the weekly shop in their red M-reg. Vauxhall Astra, subsequent to which Stan buys a Lottery ticket for the Saturday draw, washes the car, and fills up with petrol while Valerie checks to see what George has got to offer in the clothes department before they meet up again in the cafe afterwards.

'Best cup of Nescafe for many a mile,' swears Stan when occasion presents itself. 'And out of a coffee machine too. Pity George don't buck his ideas up likewise. Because George never has nowt goes anywhere near us, George's XL sizes being just about big enough to fit an XL-size Chinee,' is Stan's opinion, Stan very much regretting being constrained to pay Debenham's and BHS prices to clothe his 44 inch girth and torso on a school caretaker's take-home pay.

Stan's dog Belize (named for Stan's last overseas posting prior to his return to civilian life) chomps agreement at his feet, Bel's share of the Smart Price beans (no toast) being the bottom third of the can of beans that failed to make it on to Stan's plate.

Valerie is back in the kitchen now, at present running a tap.

Maundy Thursday or not, tonight will be no exception for Stan and Valerie with regard to the Pilsworth run. Stan says as much to Belize.

'Not much to ask, is it?' says Stan to Bel, Valerie still running the tap. 'Have to do it after Mass, of course – best leave early, I suppose, straight after the Communion.'

The tap is turned off. Valerie comes through for Stan's plate.

'Sweet FA!' says Stan to Valerie again. 'That's all the thanks you get. "Stan, can you just do this. Stan can you just do that . . ."'

All week long he's been at it too. Monday, it's the bin men – park inside the front gate and the gearbox goes on the dustbin cart, so he calls us out to open the side gate for the kids. Tuesday, it's somethin' else – can't remember – oh, yes: the choir. All set up in the hall for the Parents' Night – we waxed the floor for it over the weekend, remember – and the youngest King – what's 'is name? – Peter . . . No, *not* the Nativity play. This is Peter King, Val – Tuesday night, the Parents' Night. Sick as a dog in the choir, he is . . . Cute to you maybe? To me he's just another bleepin' nuisance . . . Because I'm called out to it, aren't I? Right in the middle of *Coruscation Avenue* too . . . "Ooh, what I wouldn't do for an Alfa Romeo", is it? What I wouldn't do for a few minute's peace, more like! Right dollop it was too. See what he'd had for his tea last Tuesday week . . . Stop that barking, Bel! . . . Where was I? Oh, yeah, Peter King sick all over the shop, needed a ruddy shovel to shift it . . . Well, you please yourself, Val . . . *Shark on arson glue,* as the French says: Everyone to his own taste . . . Well, it don't turn my stomach . . . Seen a three-course meal in a Naafi canteen or a Belize breakfast, you can stomach most things, I reckon. But what does stick in me craw is Laughin' Boy never says bring yer timesheet while your about it, Stan. Oh, no. Has us out a dozen times, too . . . Stop that *barkin',* Bel . . . . So that's eight hours overtime goin' beggin' at least. Not right, is it? Him on double pay in the holidays too! Tea break every ten minutes! Twenny weeks holiday a year! . . . I'll have to have a word with Alex, the shop steward. It's time somethin' was done, Val . . . Belize, stop that *bark* . . . Oh, it's the postman at the front door . . . What's *he* doin' back? Got somethin' for you, Val?'

Something, but what? Linsgreave closes the office window, straightens his tie, shrugs on his jacket, checks his reflection in the mirror above the book case, centres the knot on his tie – at which point a thought occurs to him. He opens the door of the office and steps out on to the corridor where he addresses Matthew Casio once more.

'Do you mind telling me why you're wearing trainers in school?'

'Sir?' (Amber.)

'Don't make me repeat myself, Matthew. Where are your school shoes?

School uniform: everything in two shades of blue – shirt, pullover, pants – barring the shoes (black) and the alternating stripe on the tie (white).

'In class, sir.' (Amber, red.)

'Why are you wearing trainers?

''S me birthday, sir. They're a birthday present, sir. Me uncle Mikey bought 'em for me for me birthday, sir, an' me mam says . . .' (Red.)

Mikey The Gun!

Linsgreave looks as one might expect of someone confronted by Mikey The Gun – the gun (a Purdy, sawn-off) being Mikey's weapon of choice, so it is said, though not in court apparently, and certainly not on this most recent occasion (the Ricky Ballistic case), where no witnesses come forward and Mikey goes free. Brother Donny too. Linsgreave's face is white now, almost grey, his words slowing in mid-flow due to his mouth and throat going dry. He burbles Dalek-like.

'Get . . . *shoe*s. . . on, Matthew'

Linsgreave is standing stock still outside his office on the ground floor corridor as Matthew Casio exits (stage right – amber, red, amber, red, amber, red, red). But his brain is working fast – racing, in fact. In vain though. Because it will take a good half an hour to get there, and Linsgreave is already forty-five minutes late. It's an impossibility, in fact, and Linsgreave knows it. There is no way he can get there in time. Telephone her? Another impossibility: her mobile number is unknown to him. Telephone Mr Thomas's? Not via the north Manchester Yellow Pages, you don't. Directory enquiries? Sure! Forty-five minutes late, plus half an hour to get there, plus another ten minutes being messed about by directory enquiries – whatever their number is nowadays. Seem to change it every ten minutes.

'*Should I put you through, sir?*'

'At 50p a *minute*? Of course you can put me through! And put me through to the Funny Farm while you're about it too!'

Arrange to meet her for lunch, being the day it is, then mess up big-style! *God, help us!* (He hasn't even got her a birthday card as yet!)

'Mrs Middleton.' Linsgreave, throws open the door to the secretary's room. 'I, er, I need to pop out for a few minutes, I'll, I'll take the bank if it's ready.'

The bank is *not* ready. '

'Thank Christ for that!' says Linsgreave *sotto voce*, leaving the school building on the run.

'Christ!' says Raphael S. Heathbank too, sixth in line at check-out No. 27, and unable to hide his impatience.

Of the twenty-seven checkouts at the ASDA store in Harpurhey just nineteen are numbered and, sequentially, they begin with a No. 2. Because check-out No. 1, right up close to the ice cream freezer cabinets lining the northerly wall of the store, neglects to declare itself as such. Check-out No. 1 displays instead an anonymous perspex cuboid, illuminated only when check-out No. 1 is manned. That is, at peak times only. There is no number displayed at check-out No. 13 either. The thirteenth checkout displays instead a caricatured wheelchair in profile. But, as if to compensate for the lack of enumeration elsewhere, check-outs Nos. 12 and 20, in addition to being appositely numbered, each display an oversized left ear in profile, and (bottom right) a capital T. Beyond this point check-out No. 21 is numbered, and closer still to the Customer Service desk and the entrance to the store, there are six more check-outs, each one of these devoid of numeration, but sharing between them half as many silhouetted hand baskets. At least one of these last six checkouts, the hand basket check-outs, is manned consistently from the start of business to the end. But all six hand basket check-outs are manned as Desmond Lingreave reaches check-out No. 6, with a birthday card he's selected (£1.99) and a bunch of flowers (Floral Bouquet – £3.25), and as many queues of shoppers are lined up at the six hand basket check-outs. There are queues too at the other nineteen checkouts, stretching away towards check-out No 1, illuminated now, right up close to the ice cream cabinets lining the northerly wall of the store. Indeed, how could it be otherwise at ASDA, Harpurhey, at 1.58 pm on a Thursday afternoon that is, as it happens, also Maundy Thursday afternoon, the Thursday before the Easter Bank Holiday weekend?

'Mary, I'll need some small silver and fifties when you've a minute.'

Susan Josephine Eshton (*née* Sidney – Josie to her friends) pauses momentarily, and turns away from the queue of customers stretching away from check-out No. 6 towards what is left of the seasonal display (half a dozen Milky Bar Easter eggs and a golden bunny that has lost its scut) to address her appeal to her supervisor, Mary Boothroyden, currently 'fannying about' (as Josie calls it) with two other ASDA personnel who are at present 'fannying about' too (as Bob Eshton calls it too, Josie having complained to him about it so often) at the Customer Services desk.

'*Ooh, what I wouldn't do for an Alfa Romeo?*' Josie Eshton says to husband Bob when she puts her feet up after getting in from work of a night. 'Ooh, what I wouldn't do for a job fannying about at the ASDA Customer Services desk more like!'

'Christ! Come *o-on!*' mutters Raphael S. Heathbank, snuffling – next in line in the queue backing up to the Seasonal shelves, because Raphael S. Heathbank is feeling the dead weight of that twelve pack of Carling now, the draining of which will be his personal contribution to the festivities for the first evening of the Easter Bank Holiday weekend.

Dean Martin, or somebody very much like Dean Martin – all sun tan and tonsils, croons from the roof space:

'Wear-a' nEaster bonnet, ye-eah –
all-a friz upo' 'ni', yeah!'
Bee-da pradders fella-ah,
inna Eas-ter Par-a-ade!

'Listen-a that berk,' Raphael S. Heathbank tells Linsgreave, next in line, not realising he is addressing Mr Desmond Aloysius Linsgreave, head of St Joseph's RC Primary School 'S' all right for him. Have some other mug luggin' his twelve pack of Carling for him.'

258

'Quite,' says Linsgreave behind his pocket handkerchief, an unwarranted blast into it in the offing. Because Raphael S. Heathbank has certainly been recognised by Linsgreave – or rather, Raphael S. *Huntsbank*, as Linsgreave initially misremembers the man, elder brother of Gabriel *Huntsbank* – no, Heathbank, isn't it? Gabriel 'The Groper' Heathbank, an alumnus of St Joseph's whom Linsgreave wouldn't care to boast about, or be reminded about – Gabriel Heathbank, occasional purveyor of pornographic materials whilst at the school, and last heard of as an alumnus of Strangeways Prison, Manchester.

Linsgreave, next in line to Raphael S. Heathbank, keeps these thoughts to himself behind his pocket handkerchief, the single word – 'Quite! – his only acknowledgment of Heathbank's salutation, plus – PARP! – an unnecessary snuffle and blow once he's deposited the Mixed Floral Bouquet (£3.25) and birthday card (£1.99) on the shopping conveyor belt, averting his eyes from Heathbank's the while, and hoping against hope that Heathbank doesn't recognise him and attempt to engage him in conversation.

And Heathbank does *not* recognise Linsgreave, though Josie Eshton does. But for her part Josie Eshton (Josie Sidney as was) is disinclined to engage Linsgreave in conversation, and would remain so disinclined were Linsgreave the last man on earth.

Linsgreave's treatment of her and son Sammy is the reason for Josie's firm aversion to the man. Long ago, this – long, long ago, son Sammy now having a good substitute father in his life (Bob Eshton), and working too nowadays (with Bob Eshton and brother Chas at Eshton's Car & Commercial Repairs in Blackley Village). That is to say, Sammy Sidney is now eleven years escaped from Linsgreave's influence, such as it was, when Sue was a single mother and, as such, the lowest of the low according to Linsgreave's personally perceived roster of significant others. No helper with the First Communion breakfast, she – concerts, project work, school outings, end-of-year trips: Josie Sidney was never invited to help with any of these. And she would have loved to have helped. Instead, whilst Sammy was an underachieving pupil at St Joseph of Cupertino RC Primary School (for one school year in the infant block) Josie Sidney found herself chased from pillar to post on a weekly basis throughout that same school year for dinner monies (ever in arrears), for school trip money, for raffle monies, for charitable donations, for uniform money, rather than being more appropriately referred, as she would eventually be referred (by Franny Quelch at St Athelstan's once Sammy was expelled by Linsgreave for flooding the infant quadrangle in the same week that Josie Sidney was sectioned in Park House at North Manchester General Hospital) to agencies and council departments which had been set up specifically to assist with temporary pecuniary embarrassment and associated difficulties. Neither, Josie can also recall (though not in so many words), had parental penury inclined Franny Quelch to exclude Sammy from participating in extra-curricular events, as had happened at St Joseph's.

'Oops!'

Josie drops Linsgreave's greetings card to the side of her chair where some idiot has spilled cat litter earlier today. The bouquet of flowers follows the card, though its greater bulk sees it makes it only halfway to the floor.

'I seem to be all thumbs today,' says Josie quasi-apologetically and unrecognised by Linsgreave.

For there is no way Linsgreave could recognise Josie Sidney, or Josie Eshton as she is now. Because Josie Eshton has money in her pocket now, TLC at home – for her and Sammy too. Her hair is tinted, more fashionably styled. Josie has colour to her cheeks now too, better bearing, a cheery smile, lively features – a wicked tongue when she chooses. She has better clothes too. Even the ASDA uniform (an uncomplimentary green with royal blue highlights) looks better on her.

JOSIE – says a badge pinned to her left breast – Always happy to help!

Anyone but you, thinks Josie, smiling to herself.

'Can I, er, use this voucher?' Linsgreave proffers the £10 voucher received from Delta-Echo.

'Can do,' says Josie cheerfully, adding untruthfully: 'But you'll get no change if you do.'

The greetings card and the bouquet combined come to just

£5.24 in total, so Linsgreave produces a twenty. And Josie Eshton arranges via an imperceptible flick of the wrist as she passes his change across for 76p of it (in 4 denominations) to require Linsgreave to retrieve it from the floor at his feet.

'Must be catching. You all thumbs too?' Josie Eshton has a broad smile on her face as somewhere up in the roof space The Beatles, with George Harrison to the fore, sing 'Something'.

'Something?' says Mr Thomas. 'Another coffee?'

Bernadette thanks Mr Thomas, but demurs. She thinks she has overstayed her welcome as it is. Two coffees, a cappuchino, two cigarettes. Not much to show for an hour spent at Mr Thomas's over the lunch hour. Her choice as well, because it's her special day after all, he'd said. He personally prefers The Pig on the Wall for a light lunch at a venue (Droylsden, The Pig) where they're unlikely to bump into family, or anyone from their neighbourhood or the education service. But you choose, he'd said. It's your day when all's said and done. So she'd chosen one o'clock at Mr Thomas's at Hollingworth Lake, her personal favourite. And then he hadn't shown.

Okay, so Mr Thomas's is just a chip shop. But The Pig on the Wall is just a pub. And Mr Thomas's *is* a very particular kind of chip shop, with a cottage-sized cafe – ten tables in all, with a tablecloth on each table, everything spick and span, and meals around a fiver, served by attentive staff and clean toilets too, should you have need of them. Mr Thomas's reminds Bernadette of good B&B accommodation she'd known when she was younger and nobody ever thought of going abroad for summer sun.

'No. Thank you,' says Bernadette to Mr Thomas, rising from her place at the table nearest the door. 'I'm only sorry to take up so much of your time without eating.'

'That's okay.' Mr Thomas smiles. 'I'm like that myself sometimes. Can't eat when it's time to eat.'

'Yes. I'm sorry.' Bernadette's lighter and cigarettes are back in her shoulder bag. 'Can I leave the paper? Do you mind?'

'Notta tall.' Mr Thomas picks up the *Daily Mess*, folded still, places it on his tray alongside the empty coffee cup. 'We'll see you again, I hope.'

'Of course.' She turns towards the door, reaching instinctively for her car keys in the front pocket of her shoulder bag. 'I . . .'

But no further explanation is possible. In any case, there isn't very much more that can be said. Woman arranges to meet her husband; husband fails to turn up? She can't say that, can she? She can't tell the real truth either, which is that this woman's husband (Desmond *Hollow Wishes* Linsgreave), this woman's husband has very likely *forgotten* to turn up.

Still, she's outside the shop now, breathing the good spring air, glancing idly at the display of Italian ice cream, nine deep, in Mr Thomas's outside kiosk from which she would have selected – eeny, meeny, miny, mo, catch a Dalek by the toe – the mint choc chip, she thinks. Yes, she'd have gone for the mint choc chip, if things had been different.

Bernadette is surprised to find she is gritting her teeth. She'd thought she was fine. Correction: she *is* fine. She glances from the ice cream display to the reflection of the woman in the window fronting Mr Thomas's cafe, the woman who's wearing Bernadette's new spring outfit. Yes, she's fine. Apart from the mouth maybe. The mouth is a little too firmly set. What was that Siobhan Stanegate called it at the governors' *soirée* at New Year when Desmond forgot to fetch the *paté de foie gras* with him? *A moue in a million*? Yes, a *moue* in a million!

Lighten up!

Her reflection obeys her, despite appearing to have a life of its own. Because in that instant before she turns towards her car (across Lake Road, parked illicitly in the car park of the Beach Hotel), she notices her right knee stiffen. Oh, it's done and done with in a fraction of a second. But it's a definite movement for all that.

Oops! Be careful! Mustn't get knocked down crossing the road!

What is it the movement reminds her of? *Yes!* Yes, it puts her in mind of a child about to stamp its foot in a fit of pique, and it bodes no good for someone – or something.

Tipping's filling station (Esso petroleum), next to the Farmyard
Hotel, corner of Cockcroft Street/Rochdale Road, 1968

51

To the YB Homeless Group, Manchester [Recorded Delivery]

Dear Ragnhilde,
      Ref: Mr Terry Grindsbrook, 18 Langdonbeck Street
You of all people (and Rafe) must surely be aware by now (subsequent to our many telephone conversations during the past twelve months, not to mention our recent meeting) of the extent to which Edmund and I have been prepared to tolerate your client's idiosyncrasies during his tenancy of our buy-to-let property at 18 Langdonbeck Street, feeling only too conscious of our having a duty of care towards the lad just as long as we remained hopeful of a modicum of positive input from your department (e.g. rental monies being paid on time, trashed carpets etc. made good), input which, as you know, never has actually materialised.

So I can tell you that your most recent statement of negative intent, received today, is the last straw.

What I now require from you are details of your in-house complaints procedure*, if any – and I want the full details too. Please do not attempt to fob me off with an anonymous post box as you have tried to do in the past. Because what I want from you now are details sufficient to enable me to take my complaint about your department as far as the Secretary of State without stopping once along the way to ask for directions.

Do not, whatever you do, mistake the seriousness or resolution of my intent – the full details are what I require, and return post is my deadline.

Yours,
Eileen Ealingham,
Blackley, Manchester
12 December 2004

*   Cue: *a cold wind whistles through Langdonbeck Street and across the David Lewis Recreation Ground where tumbleweed travels at ground level on a horizontal trajectory towards Rochdale Road; distant traffic flow can be heard on the M60 clockwise; an owl hoots in Boggart Hole Clough adjacent to Valentine Brow, the clock at St Bartholomew's church on Bottomley Side strikes thirteen . . .*

To *You Don't Say*, the *Daily Mess*

Sir,

Ref: Landlord Accreditation: a cynical financial scam

Invalided from work some years ago, I took out a mortgage on a run-down residential property in north Manchester with the intention of renting it out as a buy-to-let.

I appointed a responsible management agent who arranged for the complete refurbishment of the place from top to bottom – roofing, rewiring, light fixtures, wall-to-wall carpets, curtains, central heating, fitted kitchen, up-rated bathroom, decorating throughout, fire and burglar alarms, secure back yard. With all these things in place it looked like a little palace, and I gave instructions for it to be rented out, preferably to DSS tenants.

Okay, I weathered the burglaries and the trashing of the place by a poor lad deemed to be "under the protection" of a gang of social do-gooders I'd love to name. And I endured too – having refurbished the place once more – the subsequent non-payment of rent due to the housing department's insistence on paying the rental monies direct to a new tenant who promptly reallocated them to his various leisure interests. And notwithstanding the aforementioned disappointments, my agent has throughout this time promptly initiated all necessary repairs at my behest immediately they have been called for.

Accordingly, I was delighted to hear about Manchester City Council's proposed Landlord Accreditation scheme, thinking the powers-that-be had seen a bit of sense at long last and wanted to differentiate between landlords like the infamous Peter Rachman and ordinary people like myself who are simply trying to do the best we can for ourselves and for our tenants.

What a dope I was! Because Manchester City Council's Landlord Accreditation scheme is nothing more than a cynical financial scam specifically designed to enable Manchester City Council to pinch £2,500+ from me every five years in addition to levying a swingeing £60 charge on an annual basis for mandatory inspection of a gas safety certificate which a Corgi gas engineer bills me less than £60 for in the first place.

So, goodbye, Manchester City Council: you finally decided me to sell up.

Yours,

Eileen Ealingham,
Blackley, Manchester
31 December, 2005

PS Should you decide to publish this letter, please do so anonymously.

Pollard's (later Ogden's) grocer's, Rennie's greengrocery, plus butcher's and news agency – adjacent to the Alliance Inn., 1958. Dr Webb's house (later a convent) is in the near distance.

52

Sky

Halloween (says Jim Harney) the last night in October, a night that means big business for the makers of horror films and carnival masks, is the vigil of All Saints, and there is nothing frightening about it at all. In fact (says Jim Harney), quite the reverse is true. For All Saints' Day and All Souls' Day, the 1st and 2nd of November usher in the month of the year when it's customary for members of the Christian community to remember loved ones who have died.

In any event (says he), this is what had brought him to St Joseph's Cemetery, Moston, to tend three family graves on the Wednesday morning of that same week in November in which he had lodged his family remembrances at St John Vianney's church on Poynter Street. Though why he should have chanced upon that other grave that day – that fourth grave about which all knowledge had been lost to his family for three generations or more (he says too), he has never been able to explain with any degree of certainty or conviction.

Not that this admitted inability on Jim Harney's part will necessarily bring the monologue to an end at this juncture. For given access to a sympathetic ear (which yours obviously is, or you'd no longer be listening to this) and more whiskey than is good for him (said whiskey being Jameson's), and ensconced in what Chrys McClintock refers to as 'the Val Doonican position' – by which he means his nibs astride a bar stool, facing the optics in the corner of the lounge bar at the North Parade beneath the 20 X 36 inch print of Millet's *The Gleaners*, framed in what Clive Bradley of Manor Arts, Middleton, calls 'the two-inch Ital, Byron' (Byron Marlfield being the licensee, though his brother Pearson is the manager), it has not been unknown for Jim Harney to suggest that he was perhaps led to that fourth grave, and under military escort at that.

His first ports of call at Moston (he tells you) are in the old part of the cemetery behind the register office and chapel. From there he will normally retrace his steps as far as the corner of the chapel, then cut across diagonally to a third plot that lies close to the Campo Santo*. But on the morning in question, instead of doing this, he took it into his head to strike out in an easterly direction, keeping in as straight a line as possible until Lightbowne Road should come into sight – an undertaking which soon proved to be impracticable due to fluctuating patterns that emerged in the alignment of the graves. Thus it was that, after going no more than a few yards on his chosen trod, Harney found himself obliged to make a detour on to a grassy track lined with those headstones of a Dickensian size and style, headstones which mark the position of the public graves, or – as some say – the subscription or paupers' graves. These evoke powerful memories of Manchester's not too distant past.

There are (Jim Harney estimates) literally hundreds of public graves at Moston, five hundred of which are to be found in the section of the cemetery into which he had strayed that day. And those five hundred graves contain upwards of ten thousand souls who passed away from this life in poverty so austere that the family purse did not run to luxuries such as life assurance sufficient to finance a private interment. The poor, the pre-War poor – the dead poor! – are buried communally as so many of them had lived. Heel to heel, head to head, close-packed, stacked, buried, shriven – this last-mentioned Christian benefit apart, they lie like so many slaves in transit in the hold of a ship at sea.

The headstones marking the public graves have inscriptions on each side, an economy which has permitted the allocation of gravesites to headstones in a ratio of two to one, and thereby, a ratio of as many as forty to one, in the allocation of names to headstones. Even so, as far as space will allow, each name is recorded in full; as is the age of the deceased plus the date of demise – the dates here encompassing, as they do, the early years of the twentieth century, the duration of the First World War, and the post-war years of continuing abject poverty for the vast majority of the local population.

* The Holy Field: so-called after an early Christian
   burial ground in Rome

How ever did he find one name amongst so many? (In his cups now, Jim Harney is bearding you still.) This is a question (he says, enunciating the fifth letter of this last word with noticeable deliberation), a ques-tion he's often asked himself – particularly in view of the fact that on the morning in ques-tion he hadn't even been looking for a name. ('No, honestly! As God is my judge!' avers Harney: unnecessarily, as it happens, since his listeners have registered no objection.) And whenever he asks himself questions of this kind (he'll tell you), or when others ask them of him, it is only by retracing in his mind the actual steps he took that morning that he is able to make any sense of it at all. 'Well, chrol-on, chronologically speaking at least,' says he.

'To begin with.' he says. 'I do remember novice . . . noticing that someone had placed a spray of floor . . . flowers by one of the headstones, an' it was at this point I began to register one or two names as I walked along. On one o' the headstones I seen, saw someone had scrubbed clean a single name, a single date . . . ' Harney commences counting now: one, two, three, four . . . ' He's using the empty spirits glasses as counters, lining them up against the hatch like a squad of militiamen. '*Fi'*,' says Jim Harney, positioning the fifth glass and stifling a belch. 'Five headstones to go before I seen, saw . . . Well, it'd stop anyone in their tracks, wun' it?' He points away to his left towards some vague sinistral location that would appear to be equidistant between the skirting board on the window wall and the banister rail leading to the buffet section. 'Well, wouldn't it?' He says more distinctly, the bar stool rocking as he steps down from it.

'Steady on,' you'll tell him.

Whereupon Jim Harney will now tell you what stopped him in his tracks: '*JAMES T. HARNEY*, it said (he says). *Died 30 Nov., 1920, AGED 6 WKS.*'

The man in the register office, the older man – Eddie Collins, supplied him with the address that clinched it.

'Eggington Street?' said Jim Harney, Eddie turning to him subsequent to studying a page in the appropriate ledger.

'Number 42.'

But there was no record of a name beginning with a "T".

'Terence,' Jim's aunt informed him in a whisper when he telephoned her later that day – which was the name that would subsequently be borne out by a copy of the child's death certificate he obtained from the Manchester Register Office.

Jim Harney's aunt – two years of age when the baby died, one of four children in the family at the time (eventually there would be seven, Jim Harney's father, Barry, being the fifth) – Jim Harney's aunt supplied him with other details too, as did his cousin Jacinta, who accessed the Commonwealth War Graves Commission's website for him on the internet.

James Terence Harney (the baby) was named for two of his uncles who died in France during the First World War: Rifleman James Joseph Harney, the 8th Battalion, the London Rifle Regiment, of Slater Street, Miles Platting and Sergeant Francis Terence Sidney, the 18th Battalion, The King's Liverpool Regiment, of Southwell Street, Harpurhey; – the very men who constitute the military escort to which Jim Harney has been known to refer in his cups.

What follow are his reasons for doing so.

Amongst the family remembrances he had left at St John Vianney's church, earlier in the week (he now tells you) were two he included as an afterthought – one, for 'All occupants of the public graves in St Joseph's Cemetery, Moston' – the other, for 'All war dead who were men of goodwill'.

Jim Harney has been known to suggest that, though a baptised innocent has no need of his prayers, it amuses him to think that the his great-uncles may well have appreciated this mention in despatches, especially if it did not fall on deaf ears unlike the mention in despatches Frank Sidney received when he saved the life of an officer at the cost of his own. Wounded in action in November, 1918, Frank Sidney succumbed to his wounds on the penultimate day of the conflict.

Completely factual though and in no way speculative at all (Jim Harney is still handling the language reasonably well before the effects of that fifth double kick in), yes, completely factual is something that occurred him later that day. 'You see, that day, the day I was at Moston – well, as sure as I'm sitting here now, it was

270

Wednesday, 11th November, 1998: the eightieth anniversary of the Armistice. (More likely than not Jim Harney will omit the 't' in the word 'Armistice'.) And I must have come across the baby's grave at about the eleventh hour.'

If you were to open an atlas at a map of northern France you would notice a trunk road, the N29, running horizontally eastwards from the town of Amiens for a distance of thirty miles or so before dropping like a stone on to the town of St Quentin close to the source of the Somme. Eighty years ago and more the N29 marked a battlefield, though nowadays it carries peacetime traffic across the level fields of Picardy. Early in November, 1999, it carried James Harney too, travelling in a hire car, twelve months on from finding the baby's grave and intent on paying his respects at the military cemeteries where his great-uncles lie buried.

Heath Cemetery at Harbonnieres, where the other Jim Harney lies, is thirteen miles east of Amiens on the south side of the road. With a complement of two thousand Allied servicemen, mainly British and Australian, it's perhaps the size of a football pitch and is surrounded by a low wall. The countryside around it is bleak and forbidding, reminiscent of Northumbria for distant visibility and of the county of Norfolk for flatness of feature. The earth beyond the cemetery wall is churned up still, though it is tractors and other farm machinery that have done this nowadays rather than the tanks and shells of old. And, quite amazingly, in this most dispiriting of locations, the Commonwealth War Graves Commission has created and continues to maintain a very superior kind of garden.

You would need a good horticulturalist's catalogue to hand in order properly to categorise the full variety of shrubs and blooms that mark the headstones at Harbonnieres. Azalea, Broom, Caryopteris, heathers, Hebe, Hydrangea, Rhododendron, roses, Sedum, Senecio, Spiraea, Viburnum – hardy perennials of every description will be found here, where the gardener has been industrious to a fault. Nothing is overgrown; nowhere has any plant been left to spread itself unchecked. The soil in front of the headstones which hosts these plants has been reduced to a fine tilth, and a colonnade of two dozen trained cherry trees – *Prunus persica* and *Prunus subhirtella Autumnalis* too – leads towards the headstones from the entrance gate where not one of the trees has been permitted to drop its leaves to the ground untended.

In their teens and twenties in the main, the servicemen who lie buried at Harbonnieres fell at the Battle of Amiens in August, 1918. And as a result of the battle conditions obtaining many of them were sadly unidentifiable because many of the headstones bear inscriptions such as this:

A SOLDIER OF THE DURHAM LIGHT INFANTRY:
KNOWN ONLY UNTO GOD

Busigny Communal Cemetery Extension, where Frank Sidney lies buried, is forty-five miles away to the north-east in the midst of countryside that is pleasantly pastoral like the South Downs or the Craven Fault. Busigny is perhaps a third the size of Harbonnieres, and some seven hundred and fifty men are buried here. Most would appear to have died of wounds in the nearby dressing-station and, since they were hospitalized before they died, none of them is anonymous and each name is listed accordingly. A solitary horse chestnut tree stands guard over the grave of one poor soul who died as late as February, 1919, and over evidence too of the serenity of the cemetery's location – conkers from the horse chestnut tree lying undisturbed on the ground as late in the year as the first week in November. A book of remembrance, snug and serviceable in its niche by the gate, provides similar proof.

In the aftermath of his trip to France Jim Harney has ceased all mention of a military escort in connection with his tale.

'And about time too,' says Benny Wessenden when Avis Humesett tells him this as he matches Eddie Ealingham pint for pint in that hollow-legged way of theirs on a Carling promotion night in the corner of the lounge bar in the North Parade beneath the print of Millet's *The Gleaners* on the second Tuesday in December prior to the new Millennium.

Avis Humesett, who was, of course, Mrs David Wilde (Idle's

wife) for a good (though Avis insists they were a 'very bad') ten years of her life, laughs at Benny's response. 'Yeah, but just wait till you hear why he . . .' Avis breaks off in mid-sentence, moving away from Benny and Eddie in the 'Corner Shop' – as Fred Swellands once christened the corner of the lounge bar in the North Parade beneath the print of Millet's *The Gleaners*. Avis has moved away to serve Barry Harney, who is rapping a ten pee coin on the bar to attract her attention.

In the preceding twelve months upwards of a dozen people – regulars like Benny Wessenden and Eddie Ealingham (who was certainly a regular until he moved to North Wales a few months back) and occasional visitors such as Don Jarvis, Vinny Kelton, Clem Hardiker, Derek Keld (Tosher Dermody last New Year's Eve, as Derek Keld can recall) – upwards of a dozen people have been treated to Jim Harney's story about his military escort.

'Where is he then, Barry?' Benny Wessenden calls across to Barry Harney at which Eddie Ealingham, weary after a sleepless night with the new baby crying all the time at his son Lambert's house, laughs hilariously.

'Eh?'

'Where's the lad? On a promise, is he?'

'Oh, he'll be in. It's early yet. Ten o'clock on the dot, he'll be in.' Barry Harney checks the time on the clock above the door to the far left, the wall clock that always runs fast (it says 10.07pm, so it could be two minutes past ten by now). Barry Harney looks behind him, calls across to two men sitting at the table next to the coat stand and the fire exit – Vic Jameson and Vinny Irlam, or the 'Septua-gents', as Eddie Ealingham continues to call them though the joke is now a few years past its sell-by date. (Fred Swellands, who used to make up a fourth with these three was eighty-nine years old when he passed away earlier on in the year.) 'Time?' says Barry, indicating his left wrist with his right index finger.

But contrary to Barry Harney's stated expectation, Jim Harney does not appear that night, for Stella Harney has other plans for him – the promise she made being to her mother, to wit, that Jimmy will drive her to the pensioners' Christmas party at St Joseph of Cupertino's Parish Hall and pick her up afterwards from

273

the Palace Theatre on Oxford Street so she won't catch flu like she did last year. So it is Wednesday evening before Jim Harney puts in an appearance at the North Parade, by which time Sergeant Benny Wessenden is on nights again and Eddie Ealingham is back in Bednewydd, North Wales.

But subject to the necessary prerequisites (indeed, perquisites) – a sympathetic ear, a goodly supply of Jameson's whiskey, the bar stool facing the optics in the corner of the lounge bar in the North Parade beneath the print of Millet's *The Gleaners* – ah yes, given these, Jim Harney will now laughingly confess that the military escort he used to go on about was pure make-believe. Then he'll tell you how he arrived at this conclusion.

It was, he says, the inscription on the headstone at Harbonnieres that gave him cause to wonder

Open wide Thine arms, Lord,
and let him rest therein,
and all of mine
who fall asleep in Thee.

These words, he'll tell you – 'Same agair, Chrys. Mek man a double!' – the words of the inscription on the headstone at Harbonnieres – were supplied by his great-grandmother: long dead, of course, and whom Jim Harney never knew. But Jim Harney will tell you too that when . . . *Oh, dear! Still it's just the glass: there's no spillage involved.* (The last time Harney told his tale, they ended up walking on broken glass behind the bar till Avis fetched a sweeping brush.) Yes, when twelve months prior to his trip to France, Jim Harney submitted written details about the finding of the child's grave to his surviving aunts, he had concluded his report with these same words. They are repeated here because they comfort him; he has long since relinquished any claim to their authorship.

Premier Academy, corner of Cambridge Road/Rochdale Road,
1958. Later a medical centre; currently a nursery.

53

Political Animals

Did you never, ever see a frog
Soap-box croak, right leg agog –
That never, ever seemed to learn:
Hopped up its ass when it tried to turn?

Did you never, ever see a toad
Directing traffic in the road?
Its arms moved left, but its heart stayed centre –
It sent folk where it hadn't meant t'.

Did you never, ever see a gerbil
Puffed up big and proud and grand till
The roof caved in and the floor gave way?
So, it burrowed and hid till another day.

Did you never, ever see a snake
That looked just like your garden rake?
Its teeth seemed friendly, its back seemed firm,
But you set it to work and watched it squirm.

Did you never, ever see a man
Who's good and wise and kind? . . . I am!
Vote for me: I'll set you free –
We'll carve a page of history!
Vote for me: I'll make you rich;
We'll climb together from this ditch . . .

. . . always provided, of course, that in the unlikely event of a further recession in world
trade as a whole, one isn't forced into the sort of situation such as we had in 1967, 1968,
1969, 1970, 1971, 1972, 1973, 1974, 1975, 1976, 1977, 1978, 1979, 1980, 1981, 1982,
1983, 1984, 1985, 1986, 1987, 1988, 1989, 1990, 1991, 1992, 1993, 1994, 1995, 1996,
1997, 1998, 1999, 2000, 2001, 2002, 2003, 2004, 2005, and 2006 under the *Plus-ça-
Bloody-Change* Administration, where one might be faced with the unenviable task of
looking just a little more closely at one's original plans relating to a more equitable
redistribution of the gross national product and my Sussex farm. However, at this particular
moment in time, I think you may safely depend upon it that . . .

Old Road (left) at its junction with Rochdale Road,
top of Valentine Brow, 1958

Mount Carmel, viewed from Old Road, 1958

54

BEE LINE

Rochdale Road, Blackley Tel. 01611234567

To the American Ambassador to the Court of St James

Your Excellency,

Please accept our personal expression of deep and heartfelt sympathy at this time, and convey this to the President of the United States of America and the American people, to Mayor Giuliani and the citizens of New York.

> Your loss is our loss,
> our prayers are yours –
> peace on earth, justice tempered by compassion,
> being just two of the aspirations we share in common.

Krishna Patel, family and workmates
Bee Line Taxicabs
Rochdale Road
Blackley
Manchester

12 September 2001

55

Up Towards the Border Gate

Nowhere is there drinking water sweeter than at Uswayford* Farm in the Cheviots, and nowhere is there wayfarer wetter than the solitary walker who, dampened by a good few buckets of the stuff, turned up there on an evening in October long ago.

It was dark when he arrived and he was tired, dog-tired. After an almost unremittingly wet and misty traverse from Byrness on the Edinburgh Road he was so tired he could have slept in the rain. But perish the thought, as, indeed, perisheth the man who would succumb to it. But, even with the mist lifting momentarily now evening had come, Jim Harney would find that the problems which had attended his journey throughout the hours of daylight were not yet over.

He had made a promising start at eight o'clock that morning, having stayed overnight at Mrs Henderson's hospitable B&B on Otterburn Green. But atop Byrness Hill rain struck – and stuck.

Houx Hill was wet, Windy Crag was wetter, Ravens Knowe and Ogre Hill were wetter still. True, there came some respite along with the Border Fence and the approach to the site of the Roman camp at Chew Green, where he imagined he heard the infant River Coquet gurgling in its grassy channel. Fool! The Coquet was laughing like a drain because from Dere Street to Clennell Street he would have rain again, though with this difference: it would henceforward be accompanied by mist so thick it would afford him just ten yards of visibility for the rest of the day.

Thank heaven, then, for the Border Fence, unerring guide of the benighted traveller and the topologically deficient: thank heaven too for the refuge hut at Yearning Saddle. (Or so he thought at the time, though later he was no longer quite so sure about this, having used up a precious half hour of daylight there when only eight hours of it had been available to him in the first

* pron. *Yoozy-ford*

280

place.) But eventually – towelled, semi-dried, dry-socked, fed, and rested – he had emerged from this haven in the hills to find identical weather conditions still obtaining and, five miles further on, that his ration of daylight had run out. Night had come, though not Uswayford Farm where he had booked to stay the night: Uswayford Farm was a mile or more down Clennell Street on the English side.

This is not a problem for the properly equipped wayfarer. The properly equipped wayfarer will proceed by torchlight, as did he . . . until (Murphy's Law) torchlight too flickered, faded, and failed. Still, not to worry, because the track along which he was now making his way (the bottom track!) was a lighter shade of grey than the darkness all around – and he could hear the sound of rushing water nearby. Surely the Usway! And then the mist lifted ever so slightly but sufficient to afford him sight of a lighted window at fifty yards distance. Safe, he thought, exulting – and let out a cry. But he wasn't safe just yet.

The Usway is a perfectly pleasant little stream – or rather *burn*, given its latitude. It is perhaps the width of an alley way and generally just a few inches deep. But on the evening in question, the Usway presented him with problems three. It barred his access to the gate to Uswayford Farm; which it runs immediately across and, though it luxuriates in a wooden footbridge, the footbridge lay upstream and unseen in darkness black as a reiver's heart. Furthermore the Usway had that day received all Cheviot rainfall that had not fetched up on him. Ergo, the Usway was in spate.

Luckily, Kenneth Oldham* was at hand, or rather his remembered reading of him was. He backed off a few steps, climbed a spit of higher ground within sight of the farm, then unpacked and used that essential piece of equipment he had backpacked from Edale – a whistle! – and blew on it then for all his worth, blew on it sufficient unto the lining up of several playgrounds of children, whereupon the farmyard came alive with two or three figures running about and waving, silhouetted in the light from the farmhouse doorway. Then a Land Rover started up, trundled out of the gate, bucketing across the Usway, and returned

The Pennine Way, Kenneth Oldham, Dalesman Publishing

with him in the passenger seat. Well, almost – though not quite. The Land Rover's front wheels made it into the farmyard all right. But an empty fuel tank dictated that its rear wheels spent the night in the Usway, whilst Jim Harney spent it in a more comfortable spot.

Had he been half an hour later, Mrs Wilkinson at the farm informed him, breaking off from watching *Emmerdale* after tea, she would have certainly telephoned the police at Morpeth to report him overdue. Mrs Henderson at Byrness had telephoned her as soon as he had set off that morning to report he was on my way. Not for twenty years, Mrs Wilkinson also said, had she heard a whistle blown in distress outside her farmyard gate. On that previous occasion the distress call had come from a squad of soldiers overdue at the Otterburn Range.

He slept like a log that night, but come morning he found his things still damp when he went to collect them from where he had left them to dry on the diesel generator in the outhouse housing the snowmobiles. He stood there for a moment, trying to marshall his thoughts with the incessant semi-quavered hammering of the generator in his ears.

One set of clothes, damp; one set of clothes, dry.

Kenneth Oldham came to his assistance once more: damp clothes for the journey; dry clothes for the night. So, on with the damp clothes – YUK! – and off across the footbridge which was now easily located in the sharp sunshine of quite a different kind of day. Up towards the Border Gate he strode with Uswayford water in his flask, a good clear day ahead of him, and Kirk Yetholm his prospect at the end of it. After twenty minutes or so of "high knee raising" (thank you, Kenneth!) damp clothes feel very much like dry.

Blackley Office, at the foot of Valentine Brow, 1958

56

To Carpetbagger, the *Fiducial Times*

Sir,

Thirty years ago, when my daughter was an employee of theirs, I bought £500's worth of ordinary shares in Rapishaw Gap, in which trading was subsequently suspended for a time. When trading resumed, in 1989, under the company's new name, Rookengate, after a reverse takeover of Withers and Pratt's, I found the value of my £500 shareholding had fallen to just £80.

Perversely perhaps, I decided not to sell but to await recovery, and eventually, five years down the line, Rookengate began to pay a small dividend. You may well imagine my surprise, then, when in June last year Rookengate informed me that my ordinary shares were now B shares; though my surprise was exceeded only by my anger when, at the end of December, Rookengate sent me a cheque for £20 with the news that my B shares had now been compulsorily purchased.

I would be interested to hear your comments concerning the legality and ethics of this further instance of financial legerdemain.

Yours,

Victor Jameson (Mr)
Blackley, Manchester
10 January, 2002

Carpetbagger says: *£20, you say? You may care to note that our racing correspondent, Hobbledehoy, has napped a four-year-old called Stakeholder Pension in the 4.25 Negative Equity Mortgage Handicap Hurdle at Sedgefield this afternoon.*

57

To Krishna Patel and family

18 September 2001

Thank you from the bottom of my heart for your kind message of comfort and support following the terrorist attacks in the United States on September the 11th. The magnificent outpouring of sympathy in Britain has deeply moved all Americans.

Your message will strengthen our resolve to fight the forces of terrorism and hatred. Freedom-loving people everywhere must come together to resist the scourge of fanaticism and reassert our common humanity.

William S. Farish
Ambassador

Photographic Index

KEY: LK = Lawrie Kaye, TB = Thomas Brooks, LHP = L H Price